CANTATE

Short chants, hymns, responses and litanies
to celebrate the worship of praise and intercession

Decani Music

First published in 2005 by Decani Music Ltd, Oak House, 70 High Street,
Brandon, Suffolk IP27 0AU

Edited by Stephen Dean
Compilation © 2005 Decani Music

ISBN 1 900314 16 9

Printed by Piggott Black Bear Limited, The Paddocks, Cherry Hinton Road,
Cambridge, CB1 8DH

This book

This book aims to provide music for all kinds of worship: the Eucharist, the heart of Christian worship; services of Word and Communion, services of prayer and adoration such as Prayer around the Cross, The Prayer of the Church (e.g. morning and evening prayer), and any other occasion. It is a complete compilation in itself and can also serve as a supplement to a parish hymnal such as *Laudate*.

To make it easier to find music for a particular purpose, the book has been divided into sections which reflect the shape of all worship:

Gathering
Asking forgiveness
Glorias
The Word of God
  Psalm responses
  Gospel Greetings
  After the Word
  Faith
Intercessions
 From Word to Table
Praise of God the Father
Praise of Jesus Christ

God of Light and Darkness
The Holy Spirit
Eucharistic Acclamations and Chants
  - Sanctus, Anamnesis, Our Father (and
    the Kingdom), Peace, Agnus Dei.
Communion
Giving thanks
Following the Lord
Blessings and Dismissals
Evening and Night

One criterion for inclusion in the book was that any piece should fit on one or two pages (which has only been exceeded in a few cases); and that most of them can be sung unaccompanied or by portable musical instruments!

Gathering & Praise

It is in response to God's call that the people of God assemble. They assemble every Sunday at the command of Jesus to 'Do this in memory of me.' They may gather several times each day for the Liturgy of the Hours. They gather in prayer groups, faith-sharing groups, and for celebrations of the great moments of life.

Whenever we gather we must first acknowledge the presence of God and each other. Coming from our different places and walks of life, where we are governed by the clock and the calendar, we need to pause a moment and adjust to God's time. We acknowledge together the greatness of God and his mercies. Praise is the most basic impulse of prayer. We call upon the Lord to be with us, knowing that he already is there but is waiting for us to turn to him with our needs.

Christ is present when the Church prays and sings.

Asking Forgiveness

As part of the introduction to worship (which includes all that happens before the Scripture readings) a Penitential Act is customary. See page 32.

Gloria

The Gloria in Excelsis has been part of worship for many centuries. It is sung in many Christian churches to conclude the introductory rites. Settings are found from page 42 on.

1 Where two or three (setting 1)

S.E. Asia

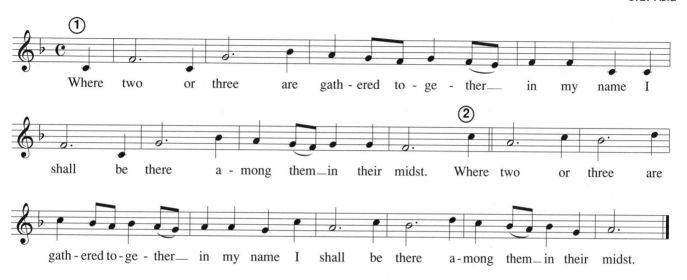

Where two or three are gath-ered to-ge-ther__ in my name I shall be there a-mong them__in their midst. Where two or three are gath-ered to-ge-ther__ in my name I shall be there a-mong them__in their midst.

This is a setting heard in Bangkok by Martin Foster. Its origins seem to be South East Asia. It may be derived from the version by Christopher Walker (no.7)

2 You have called us

Bernadette Farrell

Verses

1. You have cho-sen us to be mem-bers of your fa-mi-ly. In your
   love you have cre-a-ted us to live in u-ni-ty.

2. You will lead us to your light, walk be-fore you through the night. You will
   guide us on our jour-ney. You will keep our vi-sion bright.

3. You will hold us when we fall,
   give new strength to hear your call.
   You will never be beyond us.
   for your love is all in all.

4. You will nourish, you will lead,
   giving every gift we need,
   for your reign will be established
   from the smallest of all seeds.

5. Through our sharing here today
   may our faith and life convey
   Christ our light and Christ our vision,
   Christ our purpose, Christ our way.

3 Come all you people

Alexander Gondo
arranged by John L. Bell

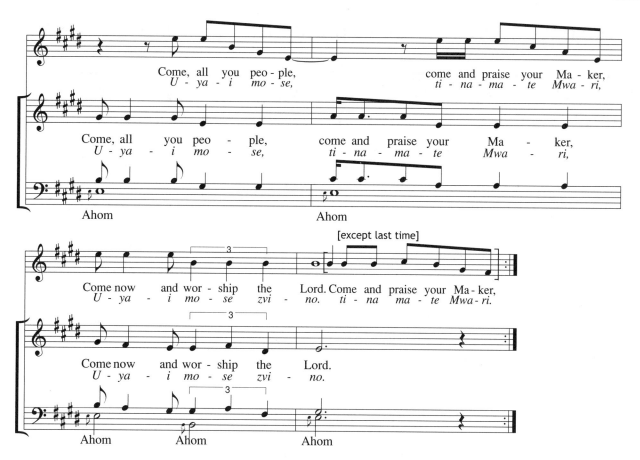

Words & Music by Alexander Gondo. Arrangement © 1995 WGRG, Iona Community, Glasgow, G2 3DH

4 Come let us seek our God's protection

Malawian folk tune, arr. Tom Colvin

1. *Come, let us seek our God's pro-tec-tion,* Ye-su sets us free to love and serve. Ye-su sets us free.

* All hum during the stanzas which are sung by a leader, or two people singing alternately.

2. Our foes are gathered all around us,

   Yesu sets us free to love and serve,
   Yesu sets us free.

3. See fear, despair and guilt enslave us,

4. Our eyes are tired from too much weeping,

5. God knows our suffering, sees our trouble,

7. How wonderful God's constant love is,

8. Our God unites us as one people,

9. Let's dance and sing to God our Saviour,

10. And shout for joy with all God's children,

11. Halleluya, yes, halleluya,

Tom Colvin

A faith-teaching song for the Church in Malawi. The melody was collected from women at Chilema in Malawi.

5 Come to us

Jo Boyce

Come to us, Come to us, li - ving Lord, li - ving Lord,

teach us how to love you, teach us how to love you.

Other texts could be sung, e.g.: *Teach us how to serve you* or *to know you*.
The assembly simply has to repeat the words sung by the cantor

6 Gather in your name

Lori True

When two or more ga-ther in your name, and see your pre-sence in each face, we

---

This song may be sung as a refrain both at the beginning and at the end of the celebration (see the alternative words in the last line), and as a Communion Song with the verses. When sung as a refrain only, it could be played through one or more times before it is sung, both make it a more substantial piece of music and to teach the tune if necessary. The singing could be repeated too.

trea-sure the gift that your word re - veals.
Comm.: trea-sure the gift of this sa - cred meal,

Come and bless us,—— here in this place.——
*Send and bless us,—— filled with your grace.——
Blessed and poured out— for all in this place.

* at the end of the celebration.

Communion Verses

Cantor/Choir

1. Bread,   the gift of your bod-y.—   Wine,—— your life blood out poured.
2. Bread,   our light and our life.   Wine,—— our truth and our way.
3. Bread,   your man - na from heav-en.—   Wine,—— the fruit of your heart.
4. Bread,   your mys-t'ry be - fore us.—   Wine,—— the hope of our dreams.
5. Bread,   the path for our jour-ney.—   Wine,—— of wis - dom and grace.
6. Bread,   the food for our long-ing.—   Wine,—— the sweet taste of love.
7. Bread   for those who seek jus-tice.—   Wine   for the hum - ble of heart.

13

Music and text © 1989
Christopher Walker. Published by
OCP Publications. All rights
reserved.

**7   Where two
or three (2)**

Christopher Walker

ALL: Come, join the feast! Take and be-lieve! Be-come what you re-ceive._____ When two or

1. 'When two   or three   are gath-ered in my name,   I am
2. Al - le - lu - ia,   al - le -   lu - ia!   I am

[1,2] there with them,____ I am there with them,____ I am there.'____

This was written as a Gospel Acclamation, but it could be sung as a gathering song, e.g. for Easter. A leader could sing it first and all repeat.

14

8 Come, ring out your joy (Psalm 95)

S.American, arr. Martin Foster

Come, ring out your joy to God. Hail the Lord, the rock who saves us. Let us

come be - fore him, gi-ving thanks, with songs let us hail⎯ the Lord. Let us come be -

fore him, gi-ving thanks, with songs let us hail⎯ the⎯ Lord.

Hanaq pachap kusikuynin was first published in 1631 in Lima. It is thought to be the first printed native American polyphony. It originally had a text in Quechua, the Inca language, and was marked to be sung in processions entering church. Here, Ps 95:1 is used as an entrance chant, to be sung as an ostinato or alternating with instruments. A simple drumbeat would be effective.

Arrangement © 2004 Martin Foster

15

9   In this place

Delores Dufner, O.S.B.,
Music: William Moore

1. In this place we come together; Faith in Jesus makes us one.
At this table let us offer praise for all our God has done.

Refrain

1–3. Thanks for life that flows around us, for your Spirit strong within, For the good we

trust will follow, for what is and what has been.

2. Here before the God of mystery
heart and voice on high we raise.
Earth and heaven here are gathered
in a hymn of cosmic praise.

3. God within and yet beyond us,
God transforming every heart,
Give us all a will to worship;
strength for service now impart.

10 Rejoice again

Christopher Walker

Re - joice in the Lord al - ways, a - gain I say re - joice.

Optional three-part ending:
Voices 1 & 2

–joice. The Lord is near, the Lord is near! A-gain, I say: Re - joice!

Voice 3

–joice. The Lord is near, the Lord is near! A-gain, I say: Re - joice!

11 Lord, draw near

John L. Bell

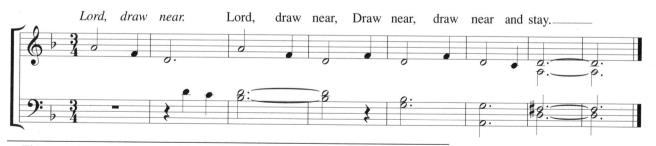

Lord, draw near. Lord, draw near, Draw near, draw near and stay.

This was written as a response to be sung during spontaneous prayers of concern. It could also be sung as part of an introductory rite, interspersing spoken texts or calls to worship.

12 All the earth, proclaim the Lord (Ps 100)

Lucien Deiss

All the earth pro-claim the Lord, sing your praise to God. 1. Serve you the Lord, hearts fill'd with glad-ness. Come in-to God's pre-sence sing-ing for joy.

2. Know that the Lord is our creator.
   Yes, God is our Father; we are his own.

3. We are the sheep of his green pasture,
   for we are God's people, chosen by God.

4. Come to the gates bringing thanksgiving,
   O enter the courts while singing in praise.

5. Our Lord is good, with love enduring,
   God's word is abiding now with us all.

6. Honour and praise be to the Father,
   the Son, and the Spirit, world without end.
   Lucien Deiss, based on Psalm 99 (100)

Response (Choir version)

All the earth pro-claim the Lord, sing your praise to God.

This setting is available in many hymnbooks but there are certain texts, like Psalm 100 (another version is *All people that on earth do dwell*) without which a book of liturgical song is incomplete.

13 I will walk in the presence of God (Ps 116)

Marty Haugen

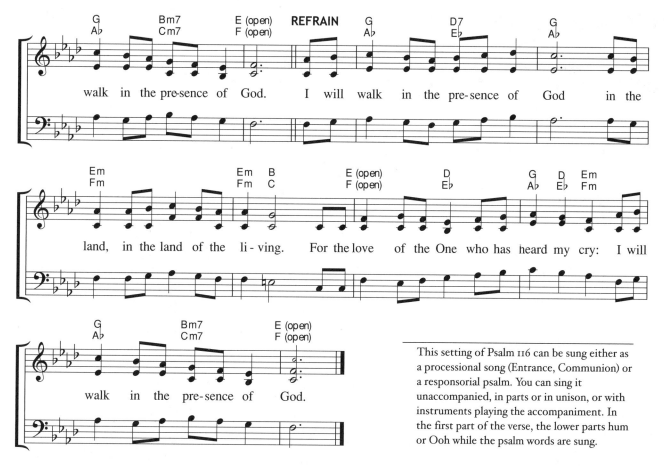

REFRAIN

walk in the pre-sence of God. I will walk in the pre-sence of God in the

land, in the land of the li-ving. For the love of the One who has heard my cry: I will

walk in the pre-sence of God.

This setting of Psalm 116 can be sung either as a processional song (Entrance, Communion) or a responsorial psalm. You can sing it unaccompanied, in parts or in unison, or with instruments playing the accompaniment. In the first part of the verse, the lower parts hum or Ooh while the psalm words are sung.

14 Let us go rejoicing (Ps 122)

Bob Hurd

1. Let us go re-joi-cing, re - joi-cing to the house of God. Let us join to-

2. Now our feet are standing
   within your gates, Jerusalem.
   Gathered as one people
   we offer thanks and praise
   before the throne of justice,
   compassion and all grace,
   rejoicing before the living God.

3. Peace reign in this city,
   the peace of God within these walls.
   May this peace empow'r us
   to put an end to war,
   to seek the reign of justice
   with dignity for all,
   rejoicing before the living God.

4. Let us go rejoicing,
   rejoicing to the house of God.
   Let us sit at table
   with Christ, the risen Lord.
   Then, guided by his Spirit
   as servants we'll go forth,
   rejoicing before the living God.

2. Washed in living water,
   we bear the name of Christ the Lord.
   We receive the mission
   to take Christ to the world,
   to be his healing presence,
   to share his saving word:

'Sending forth' text

1. Let us go rejoicing,
   rejoicing from the house of God.
   strengthened by this gath'ring
   to live the Gospel call,
   to be a holy people,
   a sacrament to all,
   rejoicing before the living God.

3. Standing with the outcast,
   the powerless, the refugee,
   with the bruised and broken
   the Church must ever be,
   a sign of hope and justice
   for all the world to see:

22

To save space, the introduction and ending have not been written separately. The (keyboard) introduction starts at the double asterisk (below *rejoicing*.) At the end of the last verse, 'rejoicing before the living God' is repeated. The *accompaniment* goes back to the beginning of the system while people are singing 'God', so there are three quavers rest before 'rejoicing...' is repeated. It's quite simple.

Music: POINT HILL, Bob Hurd, arr. Craig Kingsbury. Text and music © 1996, Bob Hurd. Published by OCP Publications. All rights reserved.

15 Our soul is waiting for God

Our soul is wai-ting for God, our hearts find joy in the Lord.

Choral harmony for verses

O_____ O_____

Verses *Superimposed on second half of chorale*
(Psalm 130:5)

1. My soul is wai-ting for the Lord: I count__ on God's word.

(Psalm 52:10)

2. I trust in the good-ness of God, for e - ver and__ e - ver.

B *(Psalm 16:1)*
3. Keep me, O God, I take re-fuge in you.

B *(Psalm 59:10)*
4. O my Strength, it is you to whom I turn. You who show me love.

B *(Psalm 59:16)*
5. As for me I will sing—— of your strength and each mor-ning ac-claim your love.

B *(Psalm 13:5)*
6. I trust in your mer-ci-ful love. My heart re-joi-ces in you.

B *(Isaiah 12:4)*
7. The Lord is my strength, my song, my sal-va-tion: in God I trust, I'm not a-fraid.

B *(Isaiah 12:4)*
8. Give thanks to the Lord, pro-claim God's deeds. Cry out for joy and glad-ness

16 The Way of the Lord (Advent Processional Song)

Martin Coster

The verses are condensed from a longer version (Decani edition 0274) which includes s an optional modulation to D for the last verse

Pre-pare his paths, re-joice in his word, We will walk in the way of the Lord.

Come, Lord, do not de-lay.

1st Sunday (this refrain may be used every Sunday)

1 Stay awake, and stand ready. *We will walk...*
Be on your guard for the Lord is coming. *We will walk ....*
Be on your guard for his day is near.

We will walk..... (as above). Vv. 2-4: opposite

2nd Sunday (ad lib.)

1 John calls us to repentance.
We prepare the way of the Lord.
Prepare the way for the Lord of mercy.
We prepare the way of the Lord.
Prepare the way for the reign of God.

We prepare the way of the Lord,
walk in his paths, rejoice in his word.
We prepare the way of the Lord.
Come, Lord, do not delay. Vv. 2-4: opposite

3rd Sunday (ad lib.)

1 Come, rejoice in our Saviour.
We rejoice in the way of the Lord.
Sing for joy: for the Lord is coming,
We rejoice in the way of the Lord.
Sing for joy: for his day is near.

We rejoice in the way of the Lord,
walk in his paths, say 'yes' to his word.
We rejoice in the way of the Lord.
Come, Lord, do not delay.

4th Sunday (ad lib.)

1 God has promised a Saviour
We say 'yes' to the way of the Lord.
from the line of the house of David,
We say 'yes' to the way of the Lord.
through the ages and for all time.
We say 'yes' to the way of the Lord.
Walk in his paths, rejoice in his word.
We say 'yes' to the way of the Lord.
Come, Lord, do not delay.

2 Come and teach us your ways, Lord.
Show us the path of peace and justice.
Show us the path of truth and love.

3 Longing, watching, and waiting
Knowing your promises will come true. Lord.
Knowing our hope is not in vain.

4 God has called us for justice:
feed the hungry; raise up the lowly.
To the poor proclaim good news.

5 *(4th Sunday)* God is with his people.
God is faithful to his promise.
Come, O Lord Emmanuel.

17 Come back to God (Lent Entrance Song)

Martin Foster

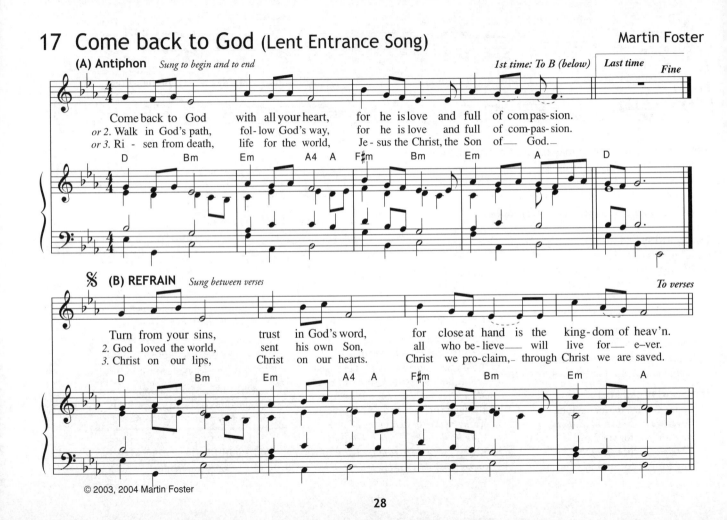

(A) Antiphon *Sung to begin and to end*

1st time: To B (below) | Last time   Fine

Come back to God with all your heart, for he is love and full of com-pas-sion.
or 2. Walk in God's path, fol-low God's way, for he is love and full of com-pas-sion.
or 3. Ri - sen from death, life for the world, Je - sus the Christ, the Son of God.

D   Bm   Em   A4 A   F#m   Bm   Em   A   D

(B) REFRAIN *Sung between verses*

To verses

Turn from your sins, trust in God's word, for close at hand is the king-dom of heav'n.
2. God loved the world, sent his own Son, all who be-lieve will live for e-ver.
3. Christ on our lips, Christ on our hearts. Christ we pro-claim, through Christ we are saved.

D   Bm   Em   A4 A   F#m   Bm   Em   A

Verses

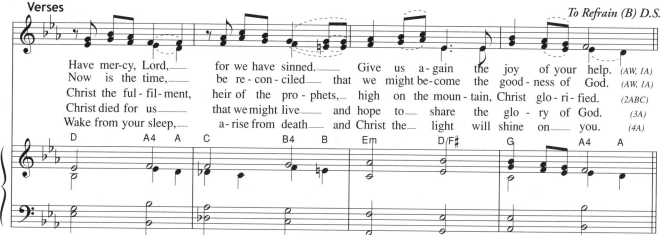

To Refrain (B) D.S.

Have mer-cy, Lord,— for we have sinned.— Give us a-gain the joy of your help. *(AW, 1A)*
Now is the time,— be re-con-ciled— that we might be-come the good-ness of God. *(AW, 1A)*
Christ the ful-fil-ment, heir of the pro-phets,— high on the moun-tain, Christ glo-ri-fied. *(2ABC)*
Christ died for us— that we might live— and hope to share the glo-ry of God. *(3A)*
Wake from your sleep,— a-rise from death— and Christ the— light will shine on— you. *(4A)*

D   A4   A   C   B4   B   Em   D/F♯   G   A4   A

Other Verses

Wait for the Lord, count on his word. For with the Lord is fullness of mercy. *(5A)*

Your ways, O Lord, are truth and love for all who keep the ways of God. *(2B)*

God did not spare his only Son, who died for us that we might live. *(2B)*

All who believe God's only Son will have eternal life through him *(4B)*

We have been saved through grace from God. We have been brought to new life in Christ. *(4B)*

Now is the hour Christ is raised up for all to see Christ glorified. *(5B)*

Deep in our hearts you place your spirit. Give us again the joy of your help. *(5B)*

Turn to the Lord in your distress. God will answer when you call. *(1C)*

God of compassion and ten der love; slow to anger, rich in mercy. *(3C)*

God reconciles the world through Christ. We will become God's goodness through Christ. *(4C)*

Forget the past and live in Christ. Through Christ's death we rise to new life. *(5C)*

The antiphon (A) is sung only at the beginning and the end; the refrain (B) after every verse. Sing verses as required. References are to Sundays in the Roman Lectionary. Full sets of verses for every Sunday in Yrs A-C are available in a separate edition (Decani 0279).

29

18 Hosanna

Bill Tamblyn

Principal Canon

Ho - san - na fi - li - o Da - vid, be - ne - dic - tus qui ve - nit in no - mi - ne Do - mi - ni. Pax in coe - lo et glo — ri - a in ex - cel - sis. Be — — dic - tus.

This was written as a Palm Sunday processional song but it could be sung on any appropriate occasion. The people can sing either the whole line or just the Assembly ostinato. Percussion parts, tuned and untuned, are available in *Easter Mysteries* (OCP) or drum parts (e.g. a triplet rhythm on one or more snare drums, timpani bass) could be improvised.

Assembly ostinato/Accompaniment

G   D   A7   D

Be - ne - dic - tus.

19 Come let us celebrate the day (Nagrikudzwe zuva)

Abraham Maraire

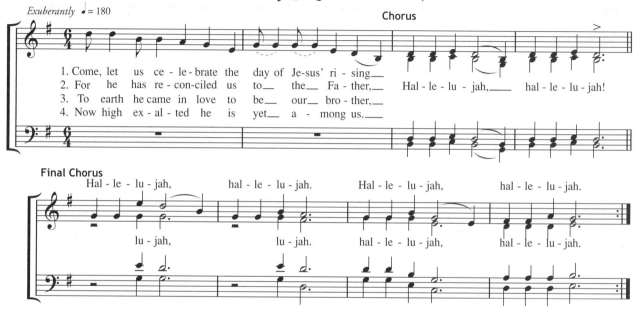

An exuberant Easter song which needs great energy (see metronome mark). There is no single way of arranging the verses, and it can last as long as seems appropriate. It is ideally accompanied on rhythmic percussion, e.g:

Another version of the final Hallelujah is at no. 59.

Asking forgiveness

20 God of mercy

Bernadette Farrell

1. God of mer-cy, you are with us. Fill our hearts with your kind - ness.
2. God of pa-tience, strong and gen-tle, fill our hearts with your kind - ness.
3. Lord, have mer-cy. Lord, have mer-cy. Lord, have mer-cy up– on us.

Ky-ri - e, ky - ri - e, ky - ri - e e - lei - son. le - i - son.

21 Kyrie eleison

Dinah Reindorf

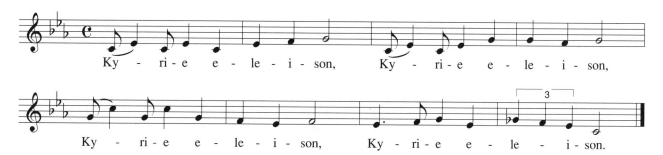

Ky - ri-e e - le - i - son, Ky - ri-e e - le - i - son,

Ky - ri-e e - le - i - son, Ky - ri-e e - le - i - son.

Optional instrumental or vocal harmony

Stephen Dean, 2002

22 Kyrie

Marty Haugen

This setting may
be used with or
without the verses,
or with spoken
invocations.

(God).
1. On my breath and in my brea-thing,___ In my laugh-ter
2. In my song and in my si-lence,___ In my faith and
3. You who know my se-cret fai-lings,___ You who touch my
4. No one el-se's love can raise me,___ No one el-se's
5. Won-drous Love that seeks and finds me,___ Word that rai-ses

Ostinato 1

Ky-ri-e e le-i-son, Chris-te e le-i-son,

A * Cantor verses start here.

and my la-bour,___ full of joy or spent in grie-ving. I call u-pon you
in my doub-ting, in my strength and in my weak-ness:
dee-pest fee-lings, know me well, and still you love me:
touch can heal me, No one el-se's voice can free me:
and un-binds me, when our sin en-slaves and blinds me:

Ky-ri-e e le-i-son, e le-i-son, e le-i-son.

6. Sun of Justice, shining o'er me,
Wind of New Life, rushing round me,
Life of ev'ry twig and blossom:

7. Rock of Ages, still support me,
Bread of New Life, still sustain me;
wine of mercy, still renew me:

8. Healing Showers, pour down on me,
Living River, swell around me,
Endless Sea of Love, surround me:

35

23 Mantra Kyrie

Christopher Walker

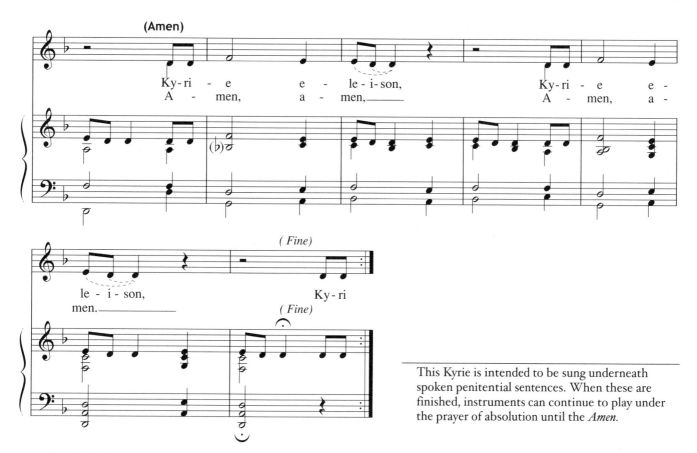

This Kyrie is intended to be sung underneath spoken penitential sentences. When these are finished, instruments can continue to play under the prayer of absolution until the *Amen*.

24 Kyrie 'Orbis Factor'

Plainchant, 10th Century

Plainchant is part of the Church's 'folk music' and is rediscovered by every new generation. This Kyrie should be sung with quiet confidence. It could be sung *a capella*, or with accompaniment of organ or voices (humming).

25 Ewuradze/Lord have mercy

from Ghana
arr. Geoff Weaver

26 Cleanse us, Lord

Christopher Willcock

This piece may be sung several times. Sections A and B may be sung in alternation by contrasting groups.

27 Create within me a clean heart

Alison Adam

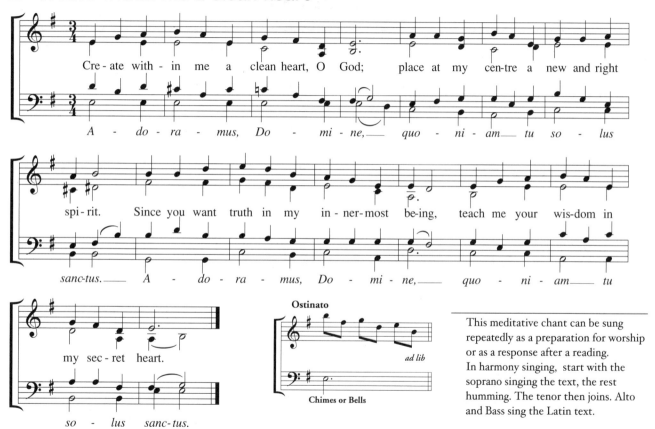

Cre-ate with-in me a clean heart, O God; place at my cen-tre a new and right

A - do - ra - mus, Do - mi - ne,— quo - ni - am tu so - lus

spi - rit. Since you want truth in my in-ner-most be-ing, teach me your wis-dom in

sanc-tus. A - do - ra - mus, Do - mi - ne,— quo - ni - am— tu

my sec-ret heart.

so - lus sanc-tus.

Ostinato

ad lib

Chimes or Bells

This meditative chant can be sung repeatedly as a preparation for worship or as a response after a reading. In harmony singing, start with the soprano singing the text, the rest humming. The tenor then joins. Alto and Bass sing the Latin text.

Paraphrase of Ps 51 and melody © 2001 Alison Adam. Arrangement by John L. Bell, © 2001 WGRG, Iona Community, Glasgow G2 3DH

Glorias

28 Argentinian Gloria

Pablo Sosa

Glo - ry, glo - ry, glo - ry, glo - ry be to God on high!

And on earth peace to the peo-ple in whom God is well pleased.

This Gloria refrain was written to be sung on its own. However, some verses have been supplied so that it may be sung as a complete setting. The verses are from the *Christmastide Gloria* from the collection *Ubi Caritas* by Bob Hurd. They can be sung by a cantor with choir vocalising the harmony.

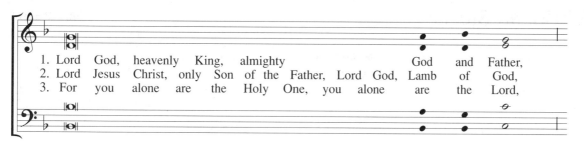

1. Lord God, heavenly King, almighty God and Father,
2. Lord Jesus Christ, only Son of the Father, Lord God, Lamb of God,
3. For you alone are the Holy One, you alone are the Lord,

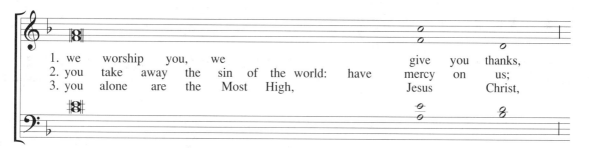

1. we worship you, we give you thanks,
2. you take away the sin of the world: have mercy on us;
3. you alone are the Most High, Jesus Christ,

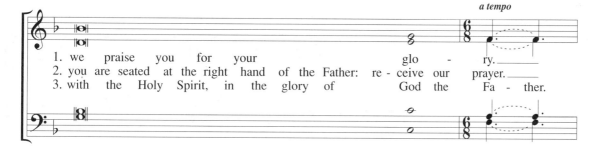

a tempo

1. we praise you for your glo - ry.
2. you are seated at the right hand of the Father: re - ceive our prayer.
3. with the Holy Spirit, in the glory of God the Fa - ther.

29 Hebridean Gloria

Barbara Rusbridge

Text and music © Barbara Rusbridge

45

30 Gloria in honour of St Jeanne Jugan

Christopher Walker

46

Music © 1982, 2001 Christopher Walker

31 Chant Glory to God

Bob Hurd

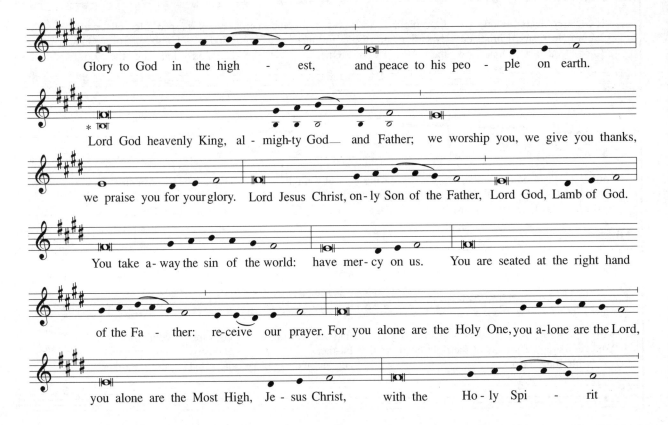

Glory to God in the high - est, and peace to his peo - ple on earth.

Lord God heavenly King, al - migh-ty God__ and Father; we worship you, we give you thanks,

we praise you for your glory. Lord Jesus Christ, on - ly Son of the Father, Lord God, Lamb of God.

You take a- way the sin of the world: have mer-cy on us. You are seated at the right hand

of the Fa - ther: re-ceive our prayer. For you alone are the Holy One, you a-lone are the Lord,

you alone are the Most High, Je - sus Christ, with the Ho - ly Spi - rit

in the glory of God the Father. A - men.

* Part of the assembly may sing the text on this pitch throughout

32 Gloria XV

Plainsong, 10th Century

Glo-ri-a — in ex-cel-sis De-o. Et in ter-ra pax ho-mi-ni-bus bo-nae vo-lun-ta-tis. Lau-da-mus te.

Be-ne - di-ci-mus te. A-do - ra-mus te. Glo-ri-fi-ca-mus te. Gra-ti-as a-gi-mus ti-bi

prop-ter mag-nam glo-ri-am tu-am. Do-mi-ne De-us, Rex cae-le-stis, Deus Pa-ter o-mni-po-tens.

This is the simplest of the plainchant Glorias, being like a psalm tone with a reciting note and phrases for beginning and ending. It should be sung without hurry, savouring the shape of the melody. If any accompaniment is wanted, a drone on A-E could be played, or a simple pattern like this:

49

Do-mi-ne Fi - li u - ni-ge-ni-te Je-su Chris-te. Do-mi-ne De-us, Ag-nus De - i, Fi - li - us Pa-tris.

Qui tol - lis pec - ca - ta mun - di mi - se - re - re no - bis. Qui tol - lis pec - ca - ta mun - di,

sus - ci - pe de - pre - ca - ti - o - nem nostram. Qui se - des ad dex - tè - ram Pa-tris, mi - se - re - re no-bis.

Quo - ni - am tu so - lus sanctus. Tu so - lus Do - mi - nus. Tu so - lus Al - tis - si - mus, Je - su Chri - ste.

Cum Sanc - to Spi - ri - tu, in glo - ri - a De - i Pa - tris. A - men.

The Word of God

Gathered in the presence of God, our next duty is to listen to the God's Word.

This section begins with songs, like the one below, which are a preparation for hearing the Word.
Some psalms follow, which allow the assembly to sing the actual words of Scripture. Next there are acclamations to greet Christ in the Gospel. This song is important in the Eucharistic ritual, but it can be sung whenever the Gospel is read.

Finally there are songs which thank God for the word received, and lead either to intercession and the end of a service of the Word, or to the table of the Eucharist.

33 Open our minds

Thomas Tallis (c.1505-85)

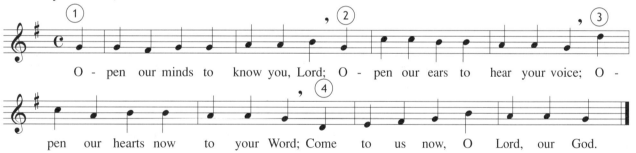

O - pen our minds to know you, Lord; O - pen our ears to hear your voice; O - pen our hearts now to your Word; Come to us now, O Lord, our God.

Open our minds to know you, Lord;
Open our ears to hear your voice;
Open our hearts now to your Word;
Come to us now, O Lord, our God.

Words by David Haas

The words may also be to be sung to the *Old Hundredth, (All people that on earth do dwell)* but Tallis' Canon allows instant harmony

34 Listen to Jesus

Christopher Walker

Written for children, this could also be sung as a Gospel Acclamation

35 Word of God

Bernadette Farrell

1. Word of God, re - new your peo - ple,
2. Word of hope and word of hea - ling,
3. Word of peace and word of jus - tice,

make us now your li-ving sign. Re-cre-ate us for your pur - pose in this place and in this time.

Written for the RCIA, this short refrain can be adapted for many occasions.

Extra verses

(Catechumenate) God alone the power we trust in ...
(Rite of Election) By your name you call us onward ...
(Lent/Good Friday) Cross of Jesus, freely chosen ....
(Lent/Good Friday) By your cross restored, forgiven ...

(Baptism/E. Vigil) To the waters lead your people ...
(Easter) Risen Saviour, with us always ...
(Mystagogy) Holy Spirit, raise your people...

36 O Word of God

Ricky Manalo

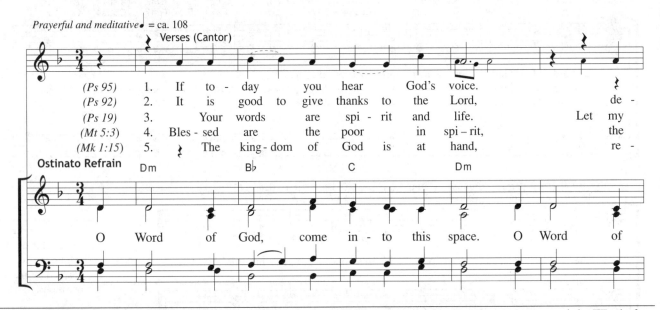

O word of God was written for faith-sharing gatherings. It is ideal for any prayer service that centres round the Word of God, such as the Liturgy of the Hours, or even before Mass as a preparation for the Liturgy of the Word.

The meditative ostinato refrain should not be rushed. At the end there is a 'musical loop' where the refrain can be picked up again by some of the singers; this creates a continuous flowing style that lends itself to prayerful meditation.

The verses are taken from those chosen by the composer and published in OCP edition O-11817, which gives a selection for each of years A, B and C.

har - den not your hearts.___
cla - ring how just is your God.___
words find fa - vour be - fore you.
king - dom of hea - ven is theirs!___
pent and be - lieve the good news!___

O - pen our minds;

God, come send us your grace. O - pen our minds; show us your

Kbd.

show us your truth. Trans - form a - new.

truth. Trans - form our lives a - new.

Kbd.   *Kbd.*

❋ *One part of the assembly may start repeating the refrain here*

55

37 Listen to the Spirit

Stephen Dean

Verses

1. *What is God say-ing?* Go and feed the hun-gry. *What is God saying?* Go and heal the sick. Hear-ken to the Spi-rit's voice, hear the words of life!

2. *What is God saying?* Welcome in the stranger.
   What is God saying? Go and heal the sick.
   Hearken to the Spirit's voice,
   Hear the words of life!

3. *What is God saying?* Give the homeless shelter.
   What is God saying? Care for those in need.
   Hearken to the Spirit's voice,
   Hear the words of life!

4. *What is God saying?* Love one another.
   What is God saying? Wash each other's feet.
   Hearken to the Spirit's voice,
   Hear the words of life!

The germ of this song is Rev. 2:7. It may
be sung is a response to the readings as
well as a preparation for them

© 2004 Stephen Dean

57

38 Word of God, burn within us

Bob Hurd

Word of God, burn with - in us, be a lamp un - to our feet.

Test our hearts and our spi - rits, true dis - ci - ples let us be.

1. Help us read the times we live in; give us eyes to see,
2. Each with gifts to build the bo- dy, ma- king it com- plete;
3. In our weak- ness, show your glo- ry, so that all may see;
4. In our gath- 'ring and our go- ing, lead us, Lord of life;

Bm A6 G6 F#m (b6) G A Bm
Dm C6 Bb6 Am (b6) Bb C Dm

Refrain D.S.

Help us tend your gro- wing King- dom, teach us how to speak.
teach us, Lord, how best to use them, ser- ving all who seek.
now no long- er I who live but Christ who lives in me.
may this lit- tle flock show forth your e- ver- las- ting life.

Bm (b6) A6 G6 F#m (b6) F Em7 G/A
Dm (b6) C6 Bb6 Am (b6) G7sus4 Gm7 Bb/C

59

39 A lamp for my feet (Ps 119)

Stephen Dean

A lamp for my steps, a light for my path, your word, O Lord, gives joy to my heart. A lamp for my steps, a light for my path, your word, O Lord, gives joy to my heart.

This psalm may be sung at Midday Prayer with verses (e.g. of Psalm 119) proclaimed by a reader. A hymn for midday prayer is no. 132

The Word of God: Psalms

The Psalter is the hymnbook of the Bible. Liturgy is unthinkable without psalm singing, whether at the Eucharist, especially as the Responsorial Psalm, or in the Liturgy of the Hours.

In this book, psalms have been dispersed throughout the volume rather than gathered into one section, in the hope that they will be better noticed this way.

This book is too small to include many complete psalms. However, it is an old tradition for the assembly to take part in psalm singing by joining in a response between sung or proclaimed verses. These psalms can be sung at any time, either on their own or with a cantor or reader singing or proclaiming the verses: at the liturgy of the hours, at the eucharist, at services of word and communion. Psalms of different character will be found in this book: psalms of praise, of thanksgiving, of lament, or penitence.

The small selection in the pages immediately following might be called Psalms of Longing. Psalms of Praise and Psalms of Confidence are mainly found in the section *God, Father and Creator* (no. 89 on, especially from no. 98.) There are also some psalms in the section on *Following the Lord* (no. 178 on), and some have been found in *Gathering* and *The Word* (such as the one opposite).

Where the verses are not provided but only a response, a reader may proclaim the psalm over the response played or hummed quietly, with everyone taking up the refrain after each verse. These short responses may be sung as Responsorial Psalms, at the Liturgy of the Hours or in prayer groups. Or the response may simply be sung on its own, without any verses.

There is a complete list of psalms on p. 286.

40   To you, O Lord, I lift my soul (Ps 25)

Marty Haugen

In the Roman lectionary Psalm 25 is one of the common psalms for Advent, and is used on several Sundays in the yearly cycle. It is also among the psalms recommended for funerals. The response given here (v.1) expresses a sentiment which would be appropriate on many occasions of formal or informal prayer.

accompaniment may be played under spoken verses.

Another version of Psalm 25 is no 181, *Jesus, Saviour.*

The full setting of this version by Marty Haugen is found in *Psalms for the Church Year Vol. 1* (GIA G-2664), as an octavo (G-2653), and in *Veni Emmanuel* (Decani).

41   O God for you I long (Ps 42)

Bernadette Farrell

O God, for you I long, more than those who watch for dawn: like the deer that yearns for wa-ter, so I thirst for you, my God.

1. Like the deer that yearns for run-ning streams, so I long for you, my
2. I drink tears as if they were my bread by night and by
3. All these things will I re-mem-ber as I pour out my
4. Why so sad with-in me, O my soul, why cast down and grie-ving
5. Still my spi-rit dies with-in me as I think of you to-
6. By day you bring me com-for in the shel-ter of your

God, and my spi-rit longs to be-hold the God of my life.
day, as I hear it said all day long 'Where is your God?'
soul, how I would lead the re-joi-cing crowd to the house of our God.
now? Hope in God; I will praise you still, my Sa-viour, my God.
day. As an ex-ile from my home-land, I cry to you, Lord.
love. By night I will sing and praise the God of my life.

D.S.

O

65

42 As the deer (Ps 42)

Jack Miffleton

As the deer longs for run-ning streams, so I thirst for you, my God.

43   My heart is searching (Ps 63)

Bob Hurd

This may be sung *a capella*. It may be repeated several times to begin prayer or study, or as a response when Ps 63 (62) occurs in the Lectionary. It may be interspersed in passages of scripture such as Matt 4:18-22, read in silence or while people hum the melody.

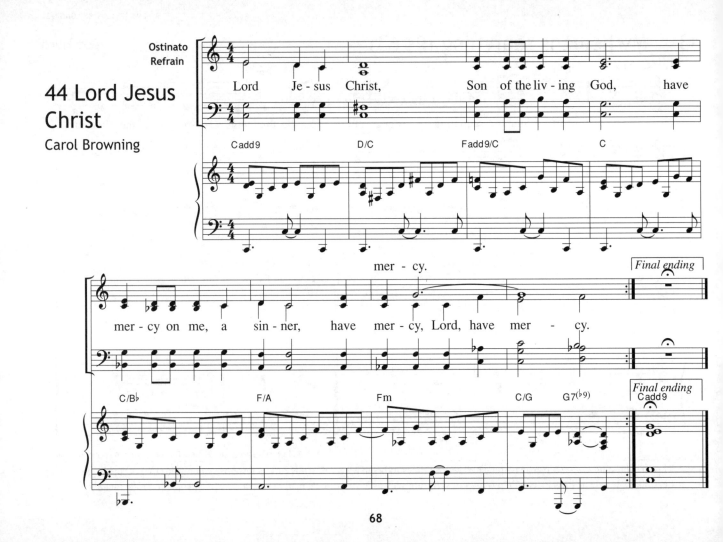

44 Lord Jesus Christ

Carol Browning

Verses *(Superimposed on Ostinato Refrain)*

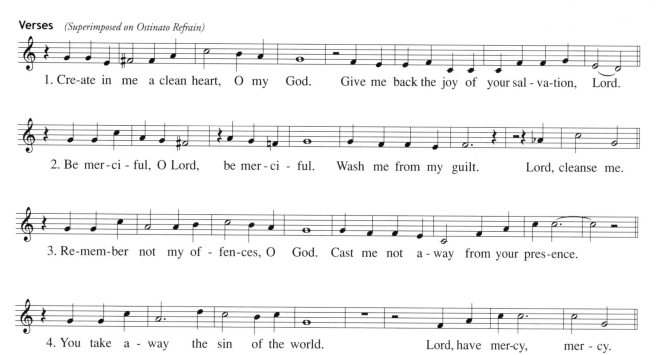

1. Cre-ate in me a clean heart, O my God. Give me back the joy of your sal - va-tion, Lord.

2. Be mer-ci - ful, O Lord, be mer-ci - ful. Wash me from my guilt. Lord, cleanse me.

3. Re-mem-ber not my of - fen-ces, O God. Cast me not a - way from your pres-ence.

4. You take a - way the sin of the world. Lord, have mer-cy, mer - cy.

This piece and the next are settings (this one with additions) of one of the greatest psalms, the *Miserere*. This is an essential part of Lent, and every Friday at Morning Prayer. It is ideal for Penitential services, or a penitential act in any liturgy. If there is no cantor to sing the verses, Psalm 51 may be read, either against a musical background or silence.

Text: The Jesus Prayer; verses, Psalm 51 and Agnus Dei, adapted by Carol E. Browning, b.1956
Tune: Carol E. Browning. Accompaniment by Kathy McGrath

45   Be merciful, O Lord (Ps 51)

Marty Haugen

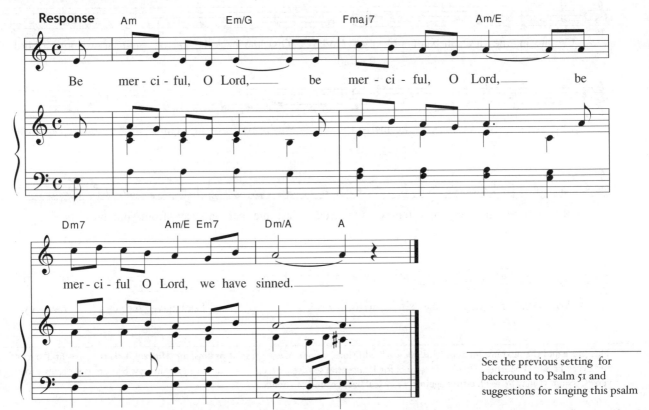

Be mer - ci - ful, O Lord,___ be mer - ci - ful, O Lord,___ be

mer - ci - ful O Lord, we have sinned.___

See the previous setting for backround to Psalm 51 and suggestions for singing this psalm

Verses

1. Have mer-cy on me, God,— in your kind-ness. In your com-pas-sion— blot out my of-fence.— O
2. For sure-ly I know— my of-fen-ces; and my sin—— is e-ver be-fore me.— A-gainst
3. A clean heart cre-ate for me, O God,— put a stead-fast spi-rit with-in me.— O
4. Give back to me the joy of your sal-va-tion; and sus-tain me with a wil-ling Spi-rit.— O

wash me more and more from my guilt,— and— cleanse—me from all of my sin.
you—— a-lone have I sinned; what is e-vil in your sight I have done.
cast me not a-way from your pre-sence, and— take— not your spi-rit from me.
Lord,—— o-pen my lips— and my mouth—shall de-clare your— praise.

71

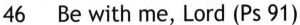

46   Be with me, Lord (Ps 91)

Marty Haugen

Be with me, Lord, when I am in trou-ble, be with me, Lord, I pray.

Verse Accompaniment (words opposite)

72

Verses

1. You who dwell in the shel-ter of the Lord Most High, who a-bide in the sha-dow of our God.

2. No e-vil shall be-fall you, no pain come near, for his an-gels stand close by your side.

3. Those who cling to the Lord live se-cure in his love, lif-ted high those who trust in his name.

Say to the Lord: 'My re-fuge and for-tress, the God in whom I trust.

Guarding you al-ways and bea-ring you gen-tly, watch-in o-ver your life.

Call on the Lord, he will ne-ver for-sake you, He will bring you sal-va-tion and joy.

Psalm 91 is a common psalm for Lent and may also be sung at Night Prayer. The psalm is much longer than the three verses given here, and other verses may be read between repetitions of the response.

47   Out of the depths (Ps 130) 1

Christopher Walker

Out of the depths I cry to you, Lord, hear my cry - ing, hear my cry - ing.

Optional verses

1. Out of the depths I cry to you, O Lord, Lord, <u>hear</u> my voice!
O let your ears be attentive to the voice <u>of</u> my pleading.

2. If you, O Lord, should mark our guilt, Lord, who <u>would</u> survive?
But with you is found forgiveness: for this <u>we</u> revere you.

3. My soul is waiting for the Lord. I count <u>on</u> God's word.
My soul is longing for the Lord more than those who <u>watch</u> for daybreak

4. Because with the Lord there is mercy and fullness <u>of</u> redemption,
Israel indeed God will redeem from all <u>its</u> iniquity.

Begin humming the melody a few times, then add the words. It may be sung as a three-part round (four bars distance), accompanied or not.

48 Out of the depths (Ps 130) 2

Stephen Dean

♩ = 80 **Optional Refrain B**

Out of the depths I cry to you, O Lord. Lord, hear my voice, Lord, hear my voice.

Principal Refrain may be sung in 2-part canon ②

De pro- fun- dis, Do- mi- ne, de pro- fun- dis cla- ma- vi ad te.

Em   Bm/D   Am/C   B   Em   Bm/D   Am/C   B

Verses

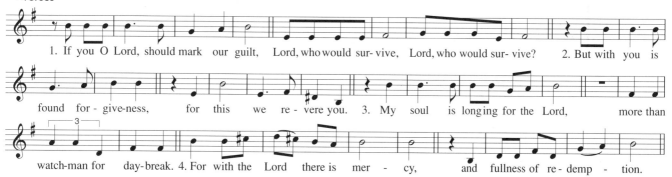

1. If you O Lord, should mark our guilt, Lord, who would sur- vive, Lord, who would sur- vive? 2. But with you is

found for- give- ness, for this we re- vere you. 3. My soul is long ing for the Lord, more than

watch-man for day-break. 4. For with the Lord there is mer- cy, and fullness of re- demp- tion.

49 Let my prayer rise
(Psalm 141, Setting 1)
Christopher Walker

*'Oo' when cantor
is singing verses

Verses (Cantor)   from Pss. 141, 26

1. Lord, hear my
2. Your love and your faith - ful - ly
3. Here in your ho - ly
4. Lord, set a
5. Lord, I will bow

voice when I call;   O hear me when I call.
ness are with me.   I praise your ho - ly name.
place I re - vere you; I give thanks for your name.
guard on my mouth.   O turn my hear from wrong.
down be - fore you.   In you my soul is at peace.

50 Let my prayer, O Lord (Ps 141, Setting 2)

Russian chant, arr. S. Dean

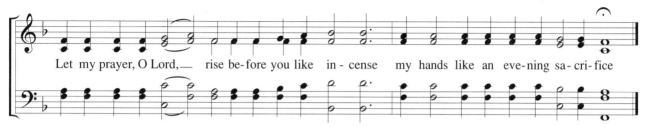

Let my prayer, O Lord, rise be-fore you like in-cense my hands like an eve-ning sa-cri-fice

Optional cantor's verses.

I have called to you, <u>Lord</u>;
has<u>ten</u> to help me.
> Hear my voice when I <u>cry</u> to you.

Set, O Lord, a guard over my <u>mouth</u>;
> keep watch, O Lord, at the door <u>of</u> my lips.
Do not turn my heart to <u>things</u> that are wrong,

May I not share in wicked men's <u>feas</u>ting.
Let the oil of the wicked not a<u>noint</u> my head.
> Let my prayer be ever a<u>gainst</u> their malice.

To you, Lord God, my <u>eyes</u> are turned;
> in you I take refuge; <u>spare</u> my soul!
Keep me from the snares of <u>those</u> who do evil.

I have called to you Lord,— has ten to help me. Hear my voice when I cry to you.

The pattern of this psalm could be: Refrain sung by all, followed by a hummed verse when the Psalm may be read or sung. It should follow speech rhythm with lengthened notes at the ends oflines. The small music example shows how the melody may be sung in the bass.

Music acc. © Stephen Dean. Text © The Grail (England)

The Word of God: the Gospel

When the Sacred Scriptures are read in the Church, God himself is speaking to his people, and Christ, present in his own word, is proclaiming the Gospel.[1]

A traditional and popular rite in the Roman liturgy is the Acclamation before the Gospel. 'By it the assembly of the faithful welcomes and greets the Lord who is about to speak to them in the Gospel, and professes its faith by singing.'[2] Note that it is not the *Gospel* that is greeted, but Christ himself.

Except in Lent, the acclamation is 'Alleluia!' In Lent, from Ash Wednesday until the Easter Vigil, other words (meaning the same thing - Praise God) are sung, so that the greeting of the risen Christ by the return of the Alleluia at Easter has more impact.

Alleluia can be sung at other times in worship. In the Easter seaon, for instance, Alleluia could be a reponse to the Psalm. It can also be sung as a response during extempore prayers of praise, or as a processional song.

---

1   General Instruction on the Roman Missal (GIRM), 29.
2   GIRM, 62

51 Listen now for the Gospel

Zimbabwe

Brightly ♩ = 120

Cantor Lis-ten now for the Gos-pel; Al-le-lu-ia! It is God's word that chan-ges us, al-le-lu-ia!

ALL *Ya-ka - na - ka Vha-nge - ri, ya-ka-na-ka! Ya-ka - na - ka Vha-nge - ri, ya-ka-na-ka!*

Al - le - lu-ia! Al-le-lu-ia!

Verses *Cantors first, All repeat*

After 2nd time, repeat Refrain D.C.

Come, Ho-ly Spi-rit, melt and break our hearts of stone, un-til we give our lives to God and God a-lone.

2. Come, Holy Spirit, root in us God's living word,
   that we may show the faithfulness of Christ our Lord.

3. Come Holy Spirit, bind the broken, find the lost,
   confirm in us the fire and love of Pentecost.

The original Shona words mean: The Gospel is good! We have already told you, it is good!

52 Alleluia

South Africa

Arrangement © Gobingca
Mxadana, c/o ISM (Pty) Ltd, PO
Box 1419, Joannesburg 2000,
Republic of South Africa

Al - le - lu - ia, al - le - lu - ia. Al - le - lu - ia, al -

le - lu - ia. Al - le - lu - ia, al - le - lu - ia. Al - le - lu - ia, al - le - lu - ia.

53 Alleluia

Palestinian traditional

Al - le - lu - ia, al - le - lu - ia, - Al - le - lu - ia, al - le - lu. Al - le - lu - ia, al - le - lu - ia, Al - le - lu - ia, al - le - lu.

Al-le-lu-ia, al-le-lu. Al-le-lu-ia, al-le-lu. Al-le-lu-ia, al-le-lu-ia, Al-le-lu-ia, al-le-lu.

54 Alleluia

Honduran traditional

Al-le lu - ia, al - le lu - ia. Al-le - lu - ia, al - le - lu - ia. Al-le - lu - ia, al - le -

lu - ia, El Se - ñor re - sus - ci - tò.

Last line can be sung: 'for the Lord is risen indeed.'

These three traditional settings which should be used in imaginative ways. The South African setting should be sung quite slowly and if possible in harmony. The other two offer possibilities for instruments and percussion.

55 Gospel Greeting: Advent, Christmas, Easter

Bernadette Farrell

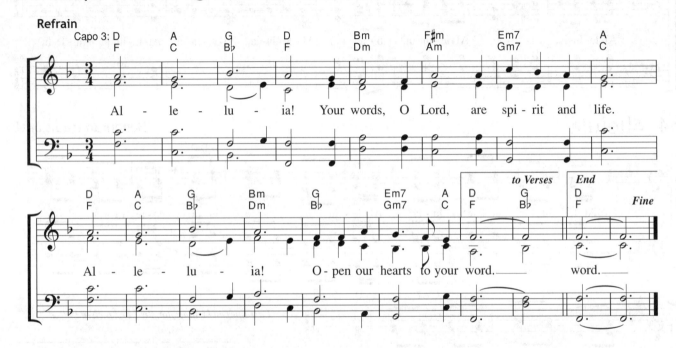

This setting could be used without the verses at other times of the year, but it is good to mark out the seasons by giving them their own distinctive music.

For an introduction, play the last four bars of the refrain, from 'Open our hearts.'

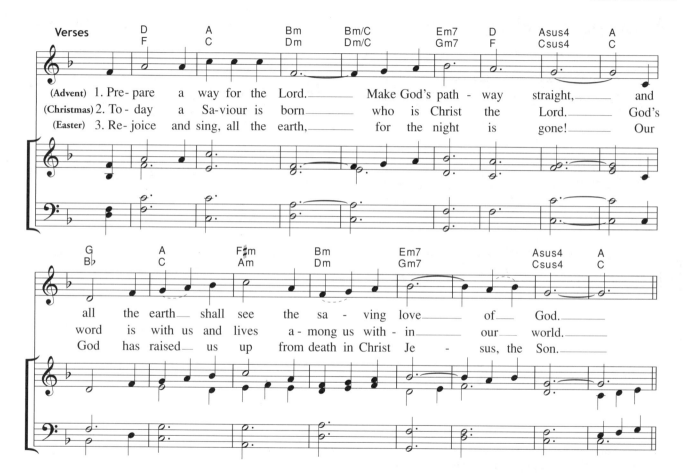

56 Gospel Greeting: Easter

Jean Tissérant

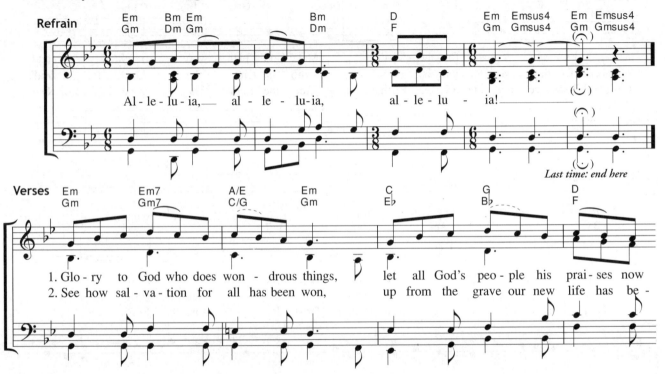

Last time: end here

1. Glo - ry to God who does won - drous things, let all God's peo - ple his prai - ses now
2. See how sal - va - tion for all has been won, up from the grave our new life has be -

---

The name of this tune, *O filii et filiae,* comes from the first words of its original text, *You sons and daughters of the Lord.*
This text is by Marty Haugen. It could be sung all through or using single verses on different Eastertide Sundays.

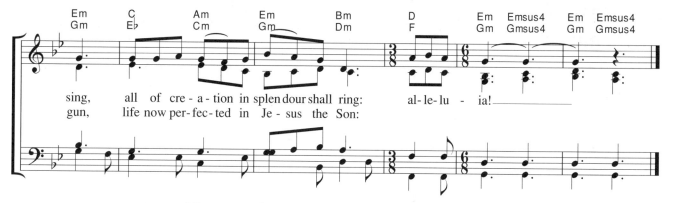

sing, all of cre-a-tion in splen dour shall ring: al-le-lu - ia!
gun, life now per-fec-ted in Je - sus the Son:

3. Now in our presence the Lord will appear,
   shine in the faces of all of us here,
   fill us with joy and cast out all our fear: Alleluia!

4. Call us, Good Shepherd, we listen for you,
   wanting to see you in all that we do,
   we would the gave of salvation pass through: Alleluia!

5. Lord, we are open to all that you say,
   ready to listen and follow your way,
   You are the potter and we are the clay: Alleluia!

6. If we have love, then we dwell in the Lord,
   God will protect us from fire and sword,
   fill us with love and the peace of his word: Alleluia!

57 'Mass of Remembrance' Alleluia

Marty Haugen

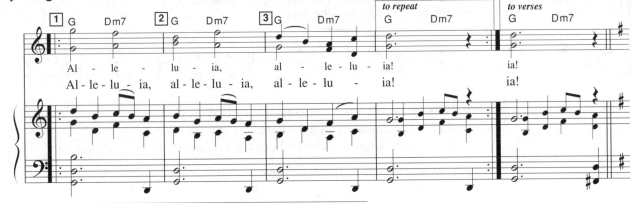

from Mass of Remembrance
© 1987 G.I.A. Publications, Inc.

1. Speak, O Lord, your ser-vant is list'-ning, you have the words of e-ver-
2. 'I am the Light of the world,' says the Lord, 'All who fol-low me shall

las - ting life.____
have the light of life.'____

3. Bles-sed are you, O Lord of cre-a-tion, re-
4. The Word of God came and lived here a-mong us, so

vea-ling your king-dom to the hum-ble and weak.
all who be-lieve might be the chi-dren of God.____

87

58 Hallelujah

Abraham Maraire

See a longer version of this song at no. 19

Music © Abraham Maraire, United
Methodist Church Service, Mutambara,
CPS Box 61, Cashel, Zimbabwe

Exuberantly ♩ = 180

Women
Hal-le-lu-jah,__ hal-le-lu-jah. Hal-le-lu-jah,__ hal-le-lu-jah.

Tenors
Hal-le-lu-jah, hal-le-lu–, hal-le-lu-jah, hal-le-lu-jah!

Basses
Hal-le-lu-jah, hal-le-lu-jah, hal-le-lu-jah, hal-le-lu-jah!

59 The Pilgrim's Alleluia

James Walsh

Intro   Capo 2: G   D   C   Am Bm   Em

Refrain 𝄋 Cantors first, then all repeat

Bm   Em   Dm   G   D   C   Am Bm   Em

Al - le - lu - ia, al - le - lu - ia, al - le - lu - ia, al - le - lu - ia.

Verses *ad lib.*

Optional Descant

1. *Strong is your love. Migh - ty your word.*
2. *Spi - rit of God, Mes - sage of truth,*
3. *All - ho - ly God: Fa - ther of Light,*
4. *Migh - ty is God, Ho - ly his name.*

1. Strong is your love. Migh - ty your word. Speak to us
2. Spi - rit of God, come fill our hearts. Mes - sage of
3. All - ho - ly God: Fa - ther of Light, Word in our
4. Migh - ty is God, Ho - ly his name. Be here with

Speak to us now, Al - le - lu - ia.
here a - mong us, Al - le - lu - ia.
Word and Spi - rit: Al - le - lu - ia.
Be here with us; Al - le - lu - ia.

now, O - pen our hearts.
truth, here a - mong us. Al - le - lu - ia.
midst, Spi - rit of love.
us; teach us your way.

60 Alleluia Beati

Christopher Walker

1. 'Bles-sed are peo-ple who know they need God. The kingdom of hea-ven be-longs— to them.'
2. O Lord, your words— give joy to my heart, your teaching, O Lord,— is light to my eyes.

Al - le - lu - ia, al - le - lu - ia! 'The king-dom of hea-ven be-longs— to them.
Al - le - lu - ia, al - le - lu - ia! Your teaching, O Lord,— is light to my eyes.

D.C. al fine

Verses for Funerals

1. Blessed are those who have died in the Lord.
   They rest from their labours, their deeds follow them.

2. 'Come, whom my Father has bless'd', says the Lord.
   'Inherit the kingdom prepared for you.'

91

61 Alleluia Mode 2

Cantor: Al - le - lu - ia.

ALL:

Al - le - lu - ia. _____ a _____ Fine

Tone for Verses

[♩ ♩]* D.S.

*The intonation may be omitted. If sung, it is only sung for the first verse

Verse (sample)

Speak, Lord, your servant <u>is</u> listening: You have the message of et<u>er</u>nal life.
I am the light of the world, says <u>the</u> Lord: anyone who follows me will have the <u>light</u> of life.

One of the simpler plainchant settings of the Alleluia, this beautiful melody is found in the *Graduale Romanum* in masses of certain saints: Stephen, both Johns, Peter and Paul. It could be sung as a Gospel Acclamation or as response to psalms which begin with the word Alleluia, e.g. 111-3, 116, 118, 135, 146-150.

62 Alleluia/Praise to you, Lord Jesus Christ

Edward McKenna

Cantor/Choir; all repeat

Al - le - lu - ia, al - le - lu - ia, al - le - lu - ia.
Praise— to you, Lord Je - sus— Christ.— King of end - less glo - ry

Verse: during the year

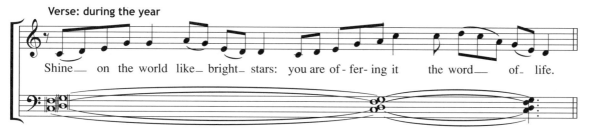

Shine— on the world like— bright— stars: you are of - fer - ing it the word— of— life.

Verse: Lent

Your— words,—Lord. are—Spi-rit and life; you—have— the mes-sage of e - ter - nal life.

A setting to be used both
in and out of Lent, to show
that it is the same Gospel
that is proclaimed the
whole year

from Irish-American Festival Mass, © 1989 Edward McKenna

63 Praise to you, O Christ

Christina Raven

Praise to you, O Christ, King of e-ter-nal glo-ry. Praise to you, Lord Je-sus Christ, King of e-ter-nal life!

1 (to repeat R.) To verses Final

Verse 1 (Ash Wednesday, General)

Har - den not your hearts, har - den not your hearts, but lis - ten to God's words, the voice of the Lord!

Verse 2 (Palm Sunday, Good Friday)

Christ was hum-bler yet, e-ven to ac-cep-ting death, but

God raised him high and named him a-bove_____ all.

Verse Accompaniment

First published in *Baptised with Fire* (Society of St Gregory, 2000), where more verses may be found.

64 Acclamation from 'Mass of Light'

David Haas

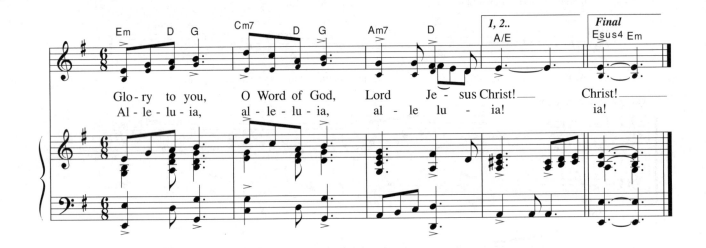

Glo - ry to you,   O Word of God,   Lord   Je - sus Christ! ___   Christ! ___
Al - le - lu - ia,   al - le - lu - ia,   al - le lu - ia!   ia!

Using the same music for Lent and Eastertide (see also no. 62) can emphazise that one season cannot exist without the other. This acclamation can be used throughout the year, in fact, and other verses are available in *Mass of Light* (GIA G-3341 FS).

1. Speak, O Lord, your ser-vant is lis-t'ning:
2. I am the way, the truth and the life.
(Lent) 3. We do not live on bread a - lone, but on

You have the words of e - ver-las - ting life.
No - one come to God, ex - cept through me.
ev - ry word that comes from the mouth of God.

97

65 Praise to you, Lord Jesus Christ

Dan Schutte

Refrain

Praise to you, Lord Je - sus Christ, Word from the heart of God.

1 (to repeat) God. *To verses* God. *Final* God.

Verses

1. If to - day you hear God's voice, do not close the doors of your hearts to the word of truth and life.
2. I will write my law on your hearts, that my word may e - ver be known, giving life to all the world.

After the Gospel

In this section are chants and songs to be sung as a response to the Word proclaimed. They could be sung in services of the Word, or of Word and Communion. Another appropriate song: no. 37

66 Your word, O Lord, is a light

Taizé

Your word, O Lord, is a light. My God, en-ligh-ten my darkness. O Lord, my
- *C'est toi ma lam-pe, Seigneur. Mon Dieu, é-clai-re ma té-nè-bre. Sei-gneur, mon*

God, en-ligh-ten my dark-ness. O Lord, my God, en ligh-ten my dark-ness.
Dieu, é-clai-re ma té-nè-bre. Sei-gneur, mon Dieu, é-clai-re ma té-nè-bre.

67 May the Word of God strengthen us

Christopher Walker

This was written for the Dismissal of the Catechumens after the Liturgy of the Word, but singing 'us' and 'ours' gives it a wider application.

Original words: May the Word of God strengthen you.
May the word of God nourish you.
May the word of God comfort you all your life.

1. May it be your light in darkness as you walk the path of life.
2. May it lead you to the freedom of the love that calls your name.
3. May it set your hearts on fire to be faithful to God's voice.

1-3 (optional)

Final

May the word of God com-fort us____ all our life.____ life.____

Optional Verses

1. May it be our* light in dark-ness____ as we* walk the path of life.
2. May it lead us to the free-dom____ of the love that calls our name.
3. May it set our hearts on fire____ to be faith - ful to God's voice.

Profession of Faith

Every act of singing to God is a profession of faith. Sometimes though, for example at baptism, confirmation and Easter (and at the Sunday Eucharist), there is an explicit profession of faith: *We* (or *I*) *believe*. These are not complete statements of everything the Gospel teaches. No creed says 'love one another' or 'Jesus Christ be praised!' They are statements about God in three persons, Creator, Redeemer and Comforter.

68 Renewal of Baptismal Promises

Martin Foster

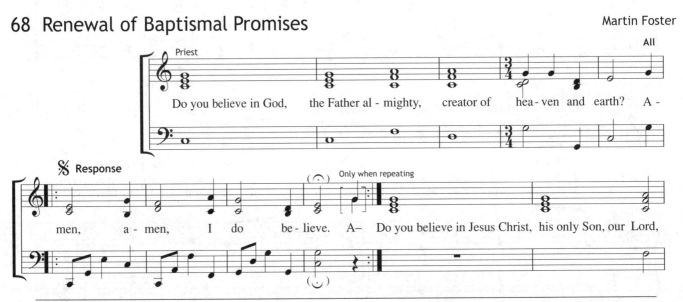

This may also be used as a response during a spoken (or chanted) recital of the Creed by the presider. See also p. 222, no 168.

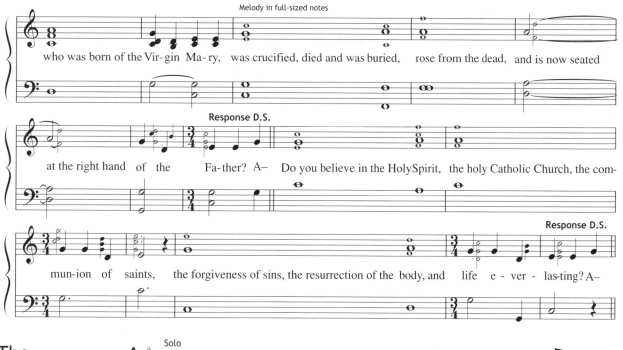

who was born of the Vir-gin Ma-ry, was crucified, died and was buried, rose from the dead, and is now seated

at the right hand of the Fa-ther? A— Do you believe in the HolySpirit, the holy Catholic Church, the com-

mun-ion of saints, the forgiveness of sins, the resurrection of the body, and life e-ver-las-ting? A—

69 The Apostles' Creed

Taizé

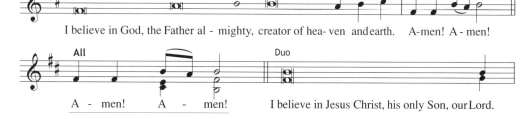

I believe in God, the Father al-mighty, creator of hea-ven and earth. A-men! A-men!

A-men! A-men! I believe in Jesus Christ, his only Son, our Lord.

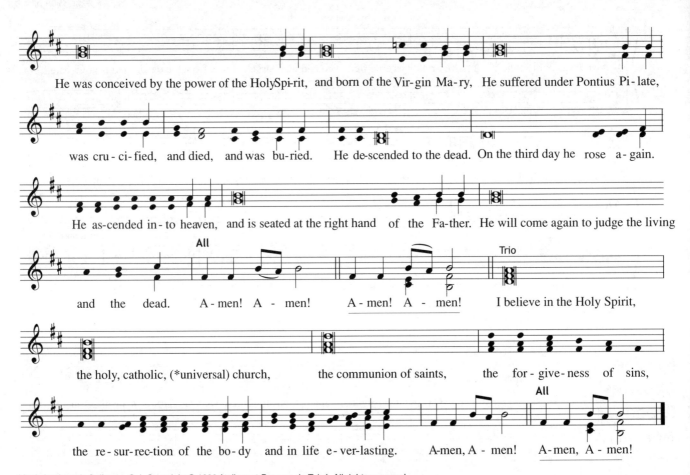

He was conceived by the power of the Holy Spi-rit, and born of the Vir-gin Ma-ry, He suffered under Pontius Pi-late,

was cru-ci-fied, and died, and was bu-ried. He de-scended to the dead. On the third day he rose a-gain.

He as-cended in-to heaven, and is seated at the right hand of the Fa-ther. He will come again to judge the living

All

and the dead. A-men! A-men! A-men! A-men!

Trio

I believe in the Holy Spirit,

the holy, catholic, (*universal) church, the communion of saints, the for-give-ness of sins,

All

the re-sur-rec-tion of the bo-dy and in life e-ver-lasting. A-men, A-men! A-men, A-men!

70 If you believe and I believe

Zimbabwe

It might be felt that this is in the wrong section, as it is really about the consequences of belief, not belief in itself. In Zimbabwe it was a liberation song ('and set Zimbabwe free') and it could be sung in prayers of intercession, naming a particular country or group of people.

71 We believe, Maranatha

Francisco Feliciano

We be-lieve: Ma-ra-na-tha, Light of the Day. We be– Day.

We be-lieve: Ma-ra-na-tha, Light of the Day. Day.

We be - lieve, we - be - lieve. lieve.

This can be sung before worship begins, or before or after the Gospel; as a canon or as a single acclamation. The Aramaic expression *Maranatha* means either 'The Lord is coming' or 'Come, Lord!' It is found only once in the Bible, at 1 Corinthians 16:20, but the words 'Come, Lord!' are almost the last words of the New Testament, Revelation 22: 20, on which this chant is based, combined with 22:5 which talks of the Light of heaven, which is God.

Prayer of Intercession

Jesus, in many parables, urges us to ask for what we need. The Lord's Prayer itself includes a series of petitions.

Prayer of intercession should follow naturally from hearing the Gospel.. We should respond to God's word in three ways: by praising God, by giving thanks for God's mercy and love, and by praying for the needs of the world, the church and ourselves personally. In this way we show that we recognise what is broken, sick and unjust, and pledge to work that it may be restored.

The introduction to the Liturgy of the Hours says: 'Jewish and Christian tradition does not separate prayer of petition from praise of God; often enough, praise turns somehow to petition.'[1] The Roman Missal says: In the general intercessions or Prayer of the Faithful, the people respond in some way to the word of God which they have welcomed in faith and, exercising a duty of their baptismal priesthood, offer prayers to God for the salvation of all.[2]

St Paul expresses it in these words:

> Rejoice always; Pray without ceasing; Give thanks in all circumstances;
> for this is the will of God in Christ Jesus for you.[3]

1: GILH 179. 2: GIRM 67 3: 1 Thess 5:16-17

See also Lord, draw near (11)
Lord's Prayer Litany (150)
Give peace in our time (155)
The face of Christ (185)

72 Kyrie 20

Taizé (Jacques Berthier)

Ky - ri - e e - le - i - son, Chris - te e - le - i - son.

© Ateliers et Presses de Taizé

73 God our Father

Stephen Dean

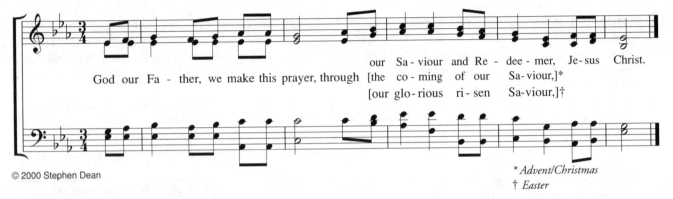

our Sa - viour and Re - dee - mer, Je - sus Christ.

God our Fa - ther, we make this prayer, through [the co - ming of our Sa - viour,]*
[our glo - rious ri - sen Sa - viour,]†

* *Advent/Christmas*
† *Easter*

74 Hear our prayer

Bob Hurd

Gospel swing ♩ = 88 (Descant last time)

Hear our prayer, hear us O

Hear our prayer. Hear our prayer. God of mer - cy,

• Verses may be altered and added to, according to local needs. Intercessions (written or spontaneous) may be spoken as well as sung

75 Lord, you alone are holy

Stephen Dean

76 Loving Father

Stephen Dean

77 Father of all

Jo Boyce and Mike Stanley

1. Fa-ther of all, lead us and guide us. The light of your Word,
shi-ning with-in us. Fa-ther, Fa-ther, Fa-ther, hear our prayer.

Chorus

Father, Fa-ther, Fa-ther, hear our prayer.

2. Father of truth,
   heal and renew us.
   Send angels of love
   to hold and protect us.

3. Father of mine,
   knowing completely
   each thought and each dream
   dwelling within me.

78 O God, hear us

Christopher Walker

Intro
♩ = ca. 76

Em Am7 Dsus 2,4 D   B/D♯ Em   C Am6 C/G Am/F♯ Bsus4 B Em

𝄋 **Response**

Em Am7 Dsus 2,4 D   B/D♯ Em   C Am6 C/G Am/F♯ Bsus4 B Em

O God, hear us, O God, hear us, in your mer - cy hear our prayer.

Tone for intercessions (Cantor)

Em   Am6/E   Bm/D C B   *D.S.*

Let us   pray   to the Lord.
or: we   pray   to the Lord.

79 Liberate us/Sikhulele

Thomzama Dyani
transcribed by David Dargie

Li-be-rate us. Lord, set us free. Lord, li-be-rate us. Lord,— set us free. Li-be-rate us.
Si-khu-lu - le Si - khu-lu - le nge-nce-ba ya - kho nko - si, si - khu-lul' si-khu-lu - le

Li-be-rate us, Lord, li - be-rate us, Lord, In your— love and mer-cy set us free.
Si-khu-lu - le Si - khu-lu - le nge-nce-ba ya-kho si - khu-lu-le.

© 1983 Thomzama Dyani & David Dargie. Administered by Choristers' Guild, 2834 Kingsley Road, Garland TX 75041

80 Send me Lord (Thuma mina)

South Africa

warmly ♩ = 76 **All**

Cantor
Thu - ma mi-na. Thu-ma mi - na, thu - ma mi - na, Thu-ma mi - na, So-mand - la.
Send me,— Lord. Send me, Je - sus, send me, Je - sus, send me Je-sus, send me, Lord.
(Lead me) (Lead me...) lead me lead me lead me
(Fill me)

© 1984 Utryck, Walton Music Corp., agent

81 Renew us, Lord

Stephen Dean

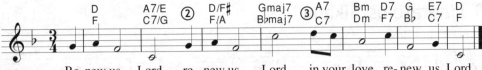

D	A7/E	② D/F♯	Gmaj7	③A7	Bm	D7	G	E7	D
F	C7/G	F/A	B♭maj7	C7	Dm	F7	B♭	C7	F

Re-new us, Lord, re-new us, Lord, in your love re-new us, Lord.

The refrain may be sung once or as a round. The accompaniment may repeat from the pause or continue to the repeat bar

Accompaniment

Finish here if only singing once

Coda

Fine

© 1996 Stephen Dean

82 O Christ, Victor

Stephen Dean

O Christ, Vic-tor o-ver death, have mer-cy on us and hear our prayer.

© 1991 Stephen Dean

114

83 Lord Jesus Christ, lover of all

John L. Bell

Lord Je-sus Christ, lov-er of all, trail wide the hem of your gar-ment, bring heal-ing, bring peace.

Lord Je-sus Christ, Lord Je-sus, lo-ver of all of all, trail wide the hem of your gar-ment, bring heal-ing, bring peace.

Lord, Je-sus Christ,— lo-ver of all, all, trail

84 Sharers in the promise

Stephen Dean

Sha-rers in the pro-mise, hea-rers of the Word, may we

work for one same King-dom, may we serve one Lord.

From Word to Table

The Liturgy of the Eucharist is only celebrated after the Word has been proclaimed. In the scriptures we hear again everything that God has done for us, and then it is our duty ('right and just') to give thanks and praise and celebrate Christ's sacrifice in memory of him in obedience to his command.

Jesus said in parable after parable that the kingdom of heaven will be like a banquet. It is feasting in common which is the most joyous thing that could be imagined. But to be called to this supper, we are asked to put our lives at God's disposal, as Jesus did on the cross, after he had given us the rite by which we should remember him.

This rite is the remembrance of a supper, at which there is a table (the altar) on which are laid symbolic food and drink over which we give thanks and praise as Jesus did. The GIRM says: 'The meaning of the [eucharistic] prayer is that the entire congregation of the faithful joins itself with Christ in acknowledging the great things God has done and in offering the sacrifice'. (78)

The songs in this section can be sung to mark the transition from the Liturgy of the Word to the Liturgy of the Eucharist.

Several other sections follow.

On page 123 a section *God our Father and Creator* which mainly includes songs of Praise, and is followed by *Psalms of Hope and Confidence* and *God of Light and Darkness*.

The section *Jesus Christ our Saviour* begins on p.159, and *The Holy Spirit* on p. 169

Making Eucharist begins on p. 178

85 Everything is yours, Lord

Zambian
arranged by Geoff Weaver

Ev-ery-thing is yours, Lord; ev-ery-thing comes from you: all we have we of-fer___ to you.
Ta-ta po-ke-le-la If-ya-bu-pe fye-su, If-yo twa-mi pe-la___ le-lo.

Ac-cept our love, Lord,___ we pray;___ re-ceive our gifts, Lord,___ to-day.
Po-ke-le-le-ni___ ta-ta,___ Po-ke-le-le-ni___ le-lo.

A song which would be very appropriate for the procession of the gifts. Varied accompaniments (particularly percussion) can be used to extend the singing as time requires. The words are from 1 Chronicles 29.

86 Song of the Body of Christ

Hawaiian melody
arr. David Haas

Verses

1. We____ come____ as your peo - ple, we come____ as your
2. We are called to heal the bro - ken, to be hope____ for the
3. Bread of life and cup of prom - ise, in this meal we all are

own, u - nit - ed with each oth - er, love finds a home.____
poor, we are called to feed the hun - gry at____ our____ door.____
one. In our dy - ing and our ris - ing, may yourking-dom come.____

D.C.

4. You will lead and we shall follow,
   you will be the breath of life;
   living water, we are thirsting for your light.

5. We will live and sing your praises,
   'Alleluia' is our song.
   May we live in love and peace our whole life long.

David Haas

119

87 Come. O come

Stephen Dean

Verses (ad lib) sung above the refrain

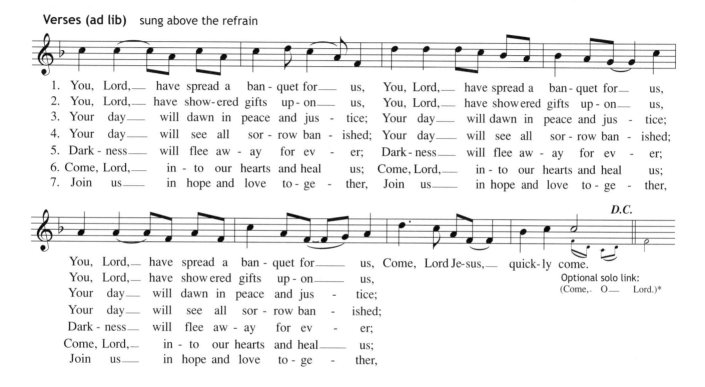

1. You, Lord,— have spread a ban-quet for— us, You, Lord,— have spread a ban-quet for— us,
2. You, Lord,— have show-ered gifts up-on— us, You, Lord,— have showered gifts up-on— us,
3. Your day— will dawn in peace and jus-tice; Your day— will dawn in peace and jus-tice;
4. Your day— will see all sor-row ban-ished; Your day— will see all sor-row ban-ished;
5. Dark-ness— will flee aw-ay for ev-er; Dark-ness— will flee aw-ay for ev-er;
6. Come, Lord,— in-to our hearts and heal us; Come, Lord,— in-to our hearts and heal us;
7. Join us— in hope and love to-ge-ther, Join us— in hope and love to-ge-ther,

D.C.

You, Lord,— have spread a ban-quet for— us, Come, Lord Je-sus,— quick-ly come.
You, Lord,— have showered gifts up-on— us,
Your day— will dawn in peace and jus-tice;
Your day— will see all sor-row ban-ished;
Dark-ness— will flee aw-ay for ev-er;
Come, Lord,— in-to our hearts and heal— us;
Join us— in hope and love to-ge-ther,

Optional solo link:
(Come,- O— Lord.)*

88 Emmaus

Bob Hurd
arr. Rick Modlin

1. Though a strang-er still un-known,— you went with them on their road, spoke to them and
2. Join us now and be our guest;— share our ta - ble, break our bread. Our hearts burn to

calmed their fears. 1, 2. Speak to us friend Je - sus; teach us, Ris - en Lord.
hear your voice.

May also be used as
a gathering song for
a prayer group.
Cantors could sing
the first part, with
all joining in at the
asterisk.

God our Father and Creator

89 Praise the Lord

Chilean

arranged by David Peacock

Praise the Lord, let us thank him for his good-ness; praise the
A - la - bad a_Jeh - o - va por-que_el es bue - no; *a - la-*

Lord, let us thank him for his good-ness; praise the Lord, let us thank him for his
bad a_Jeh - o - va por-que_el es bue - no; a - la - bad a_Jeh - o - va por-que_el es

good - ness, let's praise and a - dore him, his mer-cy lasts for ev - er!
bue - no, por - que pa - ra siem - pre es su mis - er - i - cor - dia.

This song, with words from Psalm 107, could also be used as a Gathering song.

90 You are Holy

Per Harling

You are ho- ly, you are whole;— you are al- ways so much more— than we ev- er un-der-stand.— You are al- ways at hand.— Bless- ed are you com-ing near, bless- ed are you com-ing here— to your church in wine and bread,— raised from

This lively song may be sung in canon, the second part entering where indicated.

125

91 Praise our God and Saviour

Taizé

Praise our God and Sa- viour,   O___ Praise our God and Sa- viour,   O___
Wy - sla - wiaj - cie Pa - na,   *O___*   *Wy - sla - wiaj - cie Pa - na,*   *O___*

for___ God's love en- dures for e- ver, al- le- lu - ia, al- le- lu - ia! Praise our
Spie   waj Pa - nu   ca - la - zie - mio, al - le - lu   ja, al - le - lu   ja! Wy - sla -

Verses sung over ostinato refrain

1a. With the ang-els and arch-an-gels,   with the pa- tri-archs and pro-phets.   1b. With the

Vir - gin Ma - ry, with the a - pos - tles and e - van - ge - lists. 1c. With the mar - tyrs of the faith,

all ho - ly wo - men and men. 1d. With all your Church, we give you praise.

Verse 2: Psalm 136

2a. Give thanks to the Lord, God's love en - dures for e - ver.

2b. God does great won - ders, God made the hea - vens and the earth.

2c. The Lord freed his peo - ple, and led them through the wa - ters.

2d. God led them through the de - sert, and gave them a new land.

Verse 3: Luke 1:66 ff

3a. Blessed be the Lord, who vi - sits his peo - ple. 3b. God

shows us his mer - cy, and re - mem - bers his co - ve - nant. 3c. The Lord frees us from fear,

127

so we may live from him. 3d. Be- hold the ri- sing Sun, who gives

light to those in dark-ness. 3e. The Lord guides our feet, in-to the way of peace.

92 God is forgiveness

Taizé chant

God is for-give-ness. Dare to for-give and God will be with you.

God is for-give-ness. Love and do not fear.

93 Sanna

South African, arr Geoff Weaver

94 Ever on my lips (Ps 34)

Dan Schutte

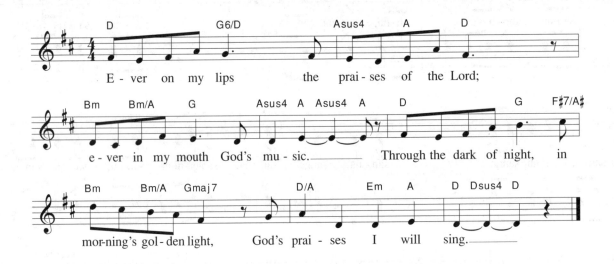

This could be sung as a refrain to many praise psalms, e.g. 96, 116 and 146.
Two descant parts (which may be played on melody instruments) and a keyboard part are on the opposite page.
The full version with verses is found in the collection *Drawn by a dream* or octavo O-10321, both from OCP

95 I will always bless the Lord (Ps 34)

John L. Bell/Traditional tune

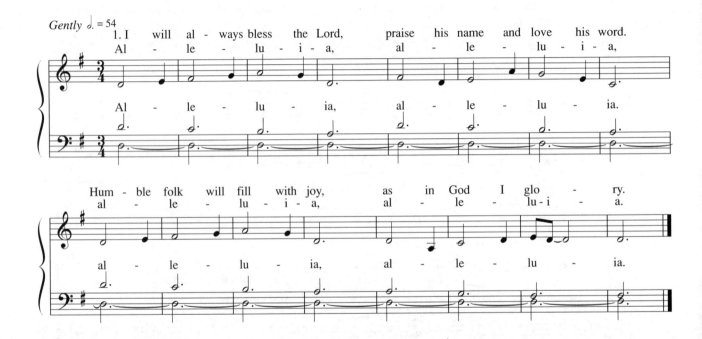

1. I will always bless the Lord,
   praise his name and love his word.
   Humble folk will fill with joy,
   as in God I glory.

2. When I prayed. God answered me,
   from my fears he set me free;
   none who trust God's faithful love
   shall be disappointed.

3. Those who cry are listened to,
   those in need receive their due;
   angels guard God's loyal folk,
   keeping them from danger.

4. Taste and see that God is good,
   know your yearnings understood,
   find your true security,
   be God's holy people.

5. *(Spoken over hummed melody by solo voice)*
   Princes may suffer hardship
   and go hungry,
   but those who wait on the Lord
   shall lack no good thing.

6. Alleluia,
   alleluia,
   alleluia,
   alleluia.

In his note to this song, John Bell writes:

'This psalm of confidence has deep significance for Celtic peoples. It is believed that St Columba of Iona, for whom copying scriptural manuscripts was a life-long activity, finished writing out the text of verse 10 shortly before he died.

Hence, it is suggested that in this setting, which goes to an ancient Gaelic lullaybe, the penultimate verse is hummed as Columba's final text is spoken, following which all sing 'Alleluia' in unison.'

He gives this scheme for singing the psalm, which should be sung *a capella*:

verse 1: solo,

2: women,

3: add bass drone,

4: add tenor,

5: all hum harmony with a voice speaking the text,

6: all sing in unison.

Glorify the Lord (Ps 34)

Stephen Dean

Glo-ri-fy, glo-ri-fy the Lord with me; to-ge-ther let us praise his name. name.

Glo - ri-fy the Lord; O praise his name. name.

Optional Verses

Instrument (or voice)

Keyboard

This refrain was originally written to be sung at Saturday Midday Prayer when this psalm occurs. The refrain may be hummed or played while the psalm verses are recited; or the optional verse below used. The Grail Psalm verses may be fitted to the top line.

Music © 2003 Stephen Dean

97 The Lord is compassion and love (Ps 103)

Stephen Dean

Music © Stephen Dean

Psalms of Hope and Confidence

98 The Lord is my shepherd (Ps 23)

Mike Stanley & Jo Boyce

Verses (spoken over accompaniment)

Final Refrain

Lord is my shep-herd, there is no-thing I shall want.

The Lord is my shep-herd, there is

The Lord is my shep-herd, there is no-thing I shall want.

no-thing I shall want.

99 Why so sad. O my soul (Ps 43)

James Walsh

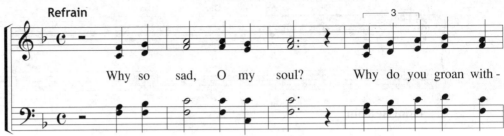

Refrain

Why so sad, O my soul? Why do you groan with-

in me? Trust in God, still I will praise my Sav-iour and my God.

Verse 1

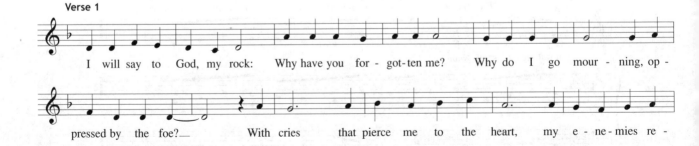

I will say to God, my rock: Why have you for-got-ten me? Why do I go mour-ning, op-

pressed by the foe? With cries that pierce me to the heart, my e-ne-mies re-

vile— me, say-ing to me all the day long, Where— is your God?

Verse 2

Pro - tect— me, O God, and de - fend me from a god-less peo-ple. Res-cue me, O God, from the de-

ceit - ful and un - just. Since you are my strong-hold, why do you re - ject me? Why do I walk in

sad - ness, op-pressed— by the foe?

Verse 3

O send— me your light and your truth, to

guide— me and lead me to your dwel - ling place on high. Then will I come to the al - tar of

God, the God who is my joy, Then will I praise you on the harp, my God,— my— God.

100   On God alone (Ps 62)

John L. Bell

On God alone I wait silently;
God my deliverer, God my strong tower.

Two settings of the same verse (Ps 62:1). The Iona version adds verse 2 as well. It is a psalm of quiet confidence in God our rock and Saviour.
More cantor verses may be found in *Taizé: Songs for Prayer* (GIA).
Either version may be sung repeatedly as a meditation or a song preparatory to worship.

101 In God alone (Ps 62)

Taizé

In God alone my soul can find rest and peace, in God my peace and joy.
â - me se re - po - se en paix sur Dieu seul: de lui vient mon sa - lut.

small notes: keyboard

Only in God my soul can find its rest,___ find its rest___ and peace. In
Oui, sur Dieu seul mon â - me se re - po - se, se re - po - sé en paix. Mon

Psalm 62:2-3

1. For God a - lone my soul waits in si - lence; from God comes my sal - va - tion.

God a - lone is my rock and my sal - va - tion.

© Ateliers et Presses de Taizé

102 I lift up my eyes (Ps 121)

Marty Haugen

♩ = c. 92-94

I lift up my eyes to the moun-tains, from where shall come my help? My help shall come from the One who has made the hea - vens and the earth, the Ma - ker of hea-ven and earth.

This Pilgrim Psalm might have been sung by travellers to Jerusalem, confident that God would protect them on the way. It could be sung at Evening Prayer (it is listed for Friday, week 2.) In the Lectionary it comes on Sunday 29 , Year C. There is a descant in GIA edition G-5228

103 You are my refuge (Ps 142)

Christopher Walker

104 You are my refuge, Lord (Ps 142)

Stephen Dean

Sample accompaniment to spoken verses

2 With all my voice I cry to you, Lord,
   with all my voice I entreat you, Lord.
3 I pour out my trouble before you;
   I tell you all my distress
4 while my spirit faints within me,
   but you, O Lord, know my path.

   On the way where I shall walk
   they have hidden a snare to entrap me.
5 Look on my right and see:
   there is no one who takes my part.
   I have no means of escape,
   not one who cares for my soul.

6 I cry to you, O Lord.
   I have said: 'You are my refuge,
   all I have in the land of the living.'
7 Listen, then, to my cry
   for I am in the depths of distress.

   Rescue me from those who pursue me
   for they are stronger than I.
8 Bring my soul out of this prison
   and then I shall praise your name.
   Around me the just will assemble
   because of your goodness to me

This very personal psalm needs no explanation: it will strike a chord with everyone. It is closely related to Ps 141 (nos 49-50) and is suitable for Evening Prayer

105 You, O Lord, are close (Ps 119)

Christopher Walker

Ostinato Refrain

You, O Lord, you are close: your ways are truth.

Verses (Cantor) Ps. 119: 145-149, 152

1. I will call with my heart. Hear me, Lord.
2. I rise be-fore dawn. I cry for help.
3. In your love, hear my voice. Give me life.

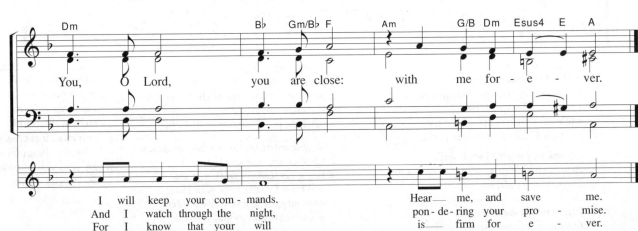

You, O Lord, you are close: with me for-e-ver.

I will keep your com-mands.
And I watch through the night,
For I know that your will

Hear me, and save me.
pon-de-ring your pro-mise.
is firm for e-ver.

106   You Lord have been my refuge (Ps 61)

Stephen Dean

---

* The verses may be sung, successively by one cantor or simultaneously by three, or played on instruments.
  This chant, like the others in this section, could be sung at healing services.

107 I wait for the Lord

Alan Shellard

I wait for the Lord, my soul doth wait. And in God's word I put my trust. I trust.

The words are actually from Psalm 130:5 but express a universal sentiment.

God of light and darkness

108 Send out your light

John L. Bell

Send out your light, Lord, send your truth to be my guide.

Then let them lead me to the place where you re - side.

109 Lord Jesus Christ

Taizé

Ostinato Chorale ♩ = 72

Lord Je - sus Christ, your light shines with in us. Let not my doubts and my darkness speak to me.
Jé - sus, le Christ, lu - mière in - té - ri - eure, ne lais - se pas mes té - nè - bres me par - ler.

Lord Je - sus Christ, your light shines with - in us. Let my heart al - ways wel - come your love.
Jé - sus le Christ, lu - mière in - té - ri - eure, don - ne - moi d'accueil - lir ton a - mour.

Verses from Psalm 139 (138)) *(superimposed on ostinato chorale)*

1. Lord, you have searched me and known me; you know when I sit down, when I rise up. You are ac quainted with

Music by JHacques Berthier (1923-1994. © Ateliers et Presses de Taizé

all my ways   2. If I take the wings of the mor-ning,   and set-tle at the far-thest li-mits of the sea,
*Choose either part

e-ven there your hand shall hold me fast. 3. If I say, 'Let the dark-ness co-ver me,'   e-ven the dark-ness is not dark to you, and

night is as bright as the day.   Search me, God, and know my heart   and lead me in the e-ver-las-ting way.

110 Our darkness

Taizé

Music by Jacques Berthier
(1923-1994.) © Ateliers et
Presses de Taizé

Bm   A   D   G

Our   dark-ness is ne-ver dark-ness in your
La té - nè - bre n'est point té - nè - bre de - vant

F#   Bm   A   D   Em   F#sus4   F#
                                              Last time

sight;   the dee-pest night is   clear   as the day —   light.
toi: la nuit com-me le   jour   est lu - miè   -   re.

151

111 Evening comes as the shadows fall (Evening Hymn)

Byzantine

Eve - ning comes as the shadows fall, while the dusk is deep-'ning and the day - light fades;

Come, ligh - ten our darkness, Lord, as our prayers rise to you, our in-cense of praise and thanks-giving.

You are the Sun that ne - ver sets, the Light of life: Ra - diance shi-ning from the Father's

---

This marvellous hymn has been sung in the East since the 2nd or 3rd century (though this music is not that old.) It can be sung as part of a Lucernarium to begin Evening Prayer. This version is more rewarding to learn in the long run, but a simpler version has been included as well.

Music: Easter chant. Words: *Phos Hilaron,* Greek, 2nd-3rd Century. English version © Pamela Stotter

glo - ry. Fill our hearts with new hope as we joy - ful - ly sing:— to the Fa - ther, Son and Spi - rit—

praise. Earth joins hea - ven as we of - fer our wor - ship. Al - le - lu - ia! A - men.

112
O gracious light

Thomas Tallis
(c.1505-85)

1. O gra - cious Light, Lord Je - sus Christ, in you the Fa - ther's glo - ry shone.
2. Now sun - set comes, but light shines forth, the lamps are lit to pierce the night.
3. Wor - thy are you of end - less praise, O Son of God, Life - gi - ving Lord:

Im - mor - tal, ho - ly, blest is he, and blest are you, his on - ly Son.
Praise Fa - ther, Son and Spi - rit: God who dwells in the e - ter - nal light.
where - fore you are through all the earth and in the high - est heaven a - dored.

113   Christ is light

Jack Miffleton

Christ is light, in him there is no dark-ness. Come to him and he will give you light.

114   O light of Christ

John Schiavone

O Light of Christ, turn our night in-to day. O Light of Christ, turn our night in-to day.

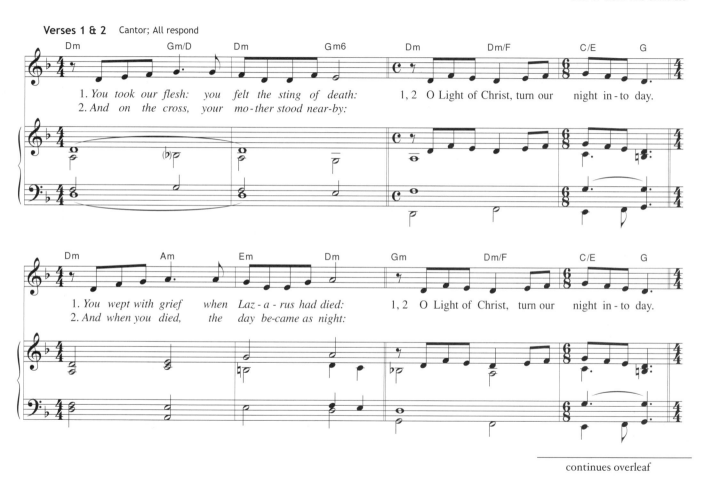

continues overleaf

1. *On your last night, you ate with dea-rest friends:*
2. *Your bro-ken flesh lay in a bor-rowed tomb:*

1, 2 O Light of Christ, turn our night in-to day.

Verses 3 & 4: Cantor; All respond

3. *On the third day, they found your emp-ty grave:*
4. *In bro-ken bread, we know that you are near:*

3,4 O Light of Christ, turn our night in-to day.

3. O Ris- en One,   you   broke the bonds of death   3.4 O Light of Christ, turn our   night in-to day.
4. Re - mem-ber   us   and   all   the ones we love:

3. Now speak to us   and   set our hearts on fire: 3,4 O Light of Christ, turn our   night in-to day.
4. In   Pa - ra-dise   with you we hope to be:

115 Come, light of the world

Martin Foster

Come, light of the world, come! Come, Christ— our light, come to re-

deem us by— your grace call us from dark-ness in-to light, come, Lord

Last time

come!—

Secondary Canon

Light of the world, come in-to our lives. Lead us from dark-ness in-to light.

Come,— light of na-tions,— light of glo-ry,— light of grace. Come, O

Last time

come!—

These two canons were written for a Candlemas procession but are appropriate all through the Advent/Christmastide season and at Evening Prayer.

Music and text © 2004 Martin Foster

Jesus Christ, our Saviour

116 Oculi nostri

Taizé

Music by Jacques Berthier (1923-94). © Ateliers et Presses de Taizé

117 Nothing can ever come between us

Taizé

Verses (Romans 8:31-39)

1. When I am a-fraid, Lord, I put my trust in you. In you I trust, I shall not fear.

2. This I know, that God is on my side. In God I trust: I shall not fear.

3. I thank you, O Lord, you saved my soul from death, so I amy walk in the light of the li-ving.

4. If it is God who jus-ti-fies, who then may con-demn? The Fa-ther gave us his own Son.

5. It is Christ who died, Christ who rose a-gain. At the right hand of God, he prays for us.

6. Nei-ther death nor life, nor things pre-sent or to come, no-thing can e-verkeep us from God's love.

© Ateliers et Presses de Taizé

161

118 Be not afraid

Be not a-fraid, sing out for joy! Christ is ri-sen al-le-lu-ia!

Be not a-fraid, sing out for joy! Christ is ri-sen, al-le-lu-ia!

119 We adore your cross

Christopher Walker

Verses *as required*

1. By your suf - fer - ing, by your hu - mi - li - a - tion:
2. By the pain you bore, strick - en for our of - fen - ses:
3. By the blood you shed, and by your con - dem - na - tion:
4. By your death, O Lord, and by your re - sur - rec - tion:

Ostinato Refrain

We a - dore your cross, O Sa - viour, and your ho - ly re - sur - rec - tion.
Cru - cem tu - am a - do - ra - mus, re - sur - rec - ti - o - nem tu - am.

hear us, hear us, O hear our prayer.
hear our prayer.
Do - mi - ne.

Hear our prayer, hear our prayer, O Sa - viour, hear our prayer.
Do - mi - ne, Do - mi - ne, lau - da - mus, Do - mi - ne.
hear our prayer.
Do - mi - ne.
hear our prayer.
Do - mi - ne.

163

120 O brother Jesus

John Bell

O bro-ther Je - sus, where have we left_ you, Sa - viour and Lo-ver of all.___

121 We adore you, O Christ

Martin Foster

Refrain

We a - dore you, O Christ, and we bless

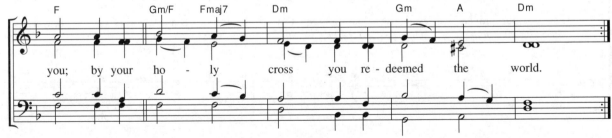

you; by your ho - ly cross you re - deemed the world.

(Optional) Verses 1-5

1. By your cross and re-sur-rec-tion; you have set your peo-ple free.
2. By the thorns that crowned your head; you have won us vic-to-ry.
3. By your limbs nailed to the cross; hands that prayed and hands that healed
4. By the lance that pierced your side; bo-dy bro-ken makes us whole.
5. By the cross of our re-demp-tion; we are re-con-ciled to God.

(Optional) Verses 6-10

6. By your death up-on the cross; you de-feat-ed death for ev-er.
7. By your rest-ing in the tomb; we have gained e-ter-nal life.
8. By your ri-sing to new life; sin is con-quered, death is slain.
9. We should glo-ry in the cross; through your death new life is gi-ven.
10. By your cross and re-sur-rec-tion; bro-ken peo-ple are made whole.

© 2002 Martin Foster

We adore you, O Christ may be sung as a response, an ostinato refrain and a processional both with and without the verses.

122 Acclamations for the Passion

Delores Dufner, O.S.B.

Matt. Glo - ry to you, O Christ, re - jec - ted and led to the cross.
Luke Glo - ry to you, O Christ, com - pas - sio - nate e - ven to the cross,

Mark Glo - ry to you, O Christ, lea - ding the way to the cross.
John Glo - ry to you, O Christ, reign - ing from the wood of the cross.

Cross of our sal - va - tion, life and re - sur - rec - tion! We glo - ry in your cross, O Je - sus Christ!

These are to be sung during the reading of the Passion Gospels. The first time , the acclamation may be sung by a cantor and repeated by all. Thereafter, all sing straight away. The final time the acclmation may be sung unaccompanied.

Text and music (tune CIFERNI): Delores Dufner, O.S.B.,
© 1994, 2003 GIA Publications, Inc.

The acclamations are sung after each section of the passion reading:

Matthew	Mark	Luke	John
26:14-29	14:1-25	22:14-38	18:1-12
26:30-56	14:26-52	22:39-53	18:13-27
26:57-27:10	14:53-72	22:54-71	18:28-19:16a
27:11-31	15:1-20	23:1-25	19:16b-42
27:32-66	15:21-47	23:26-56	

123 Christ in our joys

Martin Foster

Christ in our joys and Christ in our sor - rows. Christ in our hopes and fears for to-mor - row.*Christ in our li - ving, Christ in our dy - ing, Christ in our ri - sing, Christ our way.

© 2002 Martin Foster

*Alternative text ending: Christ in our talking; Christ in our list'ning. Christ our reflection; Christ our way.

124 Jesus, your Spirit

Taizé

Ostinato Refrain

Je - sus, your Spi - rit in us is a well-spring of life e - ver las - ting.

Verses Psalm 63

1. O God, you are my God, for you I long, my soul thirsts for you. I wish to gaze u-pon you,

Lord, in your dwel-ling, be - hol - ding your po - wer and your glo-ry. 2. Your stead - fast love is

bet - ter than life, my mouth will sing your praise. I will bless you, O Lord, as long as I live, in your

name lift up my hands. 3. You have been my help, Lord; in the sha-dow of your wings I sing for

joy. My soul clings to you, O God, your right hand holds me fast.

The Holy Spirit

125   Come, Holy Spirit 1

John L. Bell

126 Come, Holy Spirit 2

Stephen Dean

Ostinato Refrain

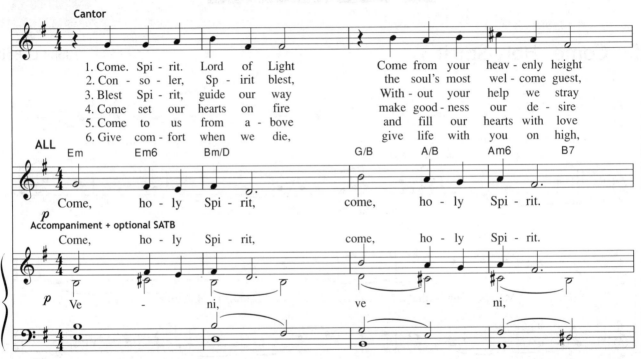

1. Come. Spi - rit. Lord of Light — Come from your heav - enly height
2. Con - so - ler, Spi - rit blest, — the soul's most wel - come guest,
3. Blest Spi - rit, guide our way — With - out your help we stray
4. Come set our hearts on fire — make good - ness our de - sire
5. Come to us from a - bove — and fill our hearts with love
6. Give com - fort when we die, — give life with you on high,

ALL

Come, ho - ly Spi - rit, come, ho - ly Spi - rit.

Accompaniment + optional SATB

Come, ho - ly Spi - rit, come, ho - ly Spi - rit.

Ve - ni, ve - ni,

This chant may be used on Pentecost Sunday (when the sequence *Veni Sante Spiritus* is to be sung), at Confirmations and prayer services, when the verses are optional. The main melody should be established before verses are added.

Come and res - tore our sight Come, O Spi - rit.
our ease in toil and stress, Come, O Spi - rit.
come to our hearts to - day Come, O Spi - rit.
our weak - ening souls in - spire Come, O Spi - rit.
Des - cend, O heav - enly Dove, Come, O Sp - rit.
un - en - ding joys sup - ply, Come, O Spi - rit.

Em/G Am Bm Am7 Em7 Bm6 Csus2 Am6

Final
Em

come, ho - ly Spi - rit set our hearts on fire.
come, ho - ly Spi - rit set our hearts on fire.

Final

ve - ni Sanc - te Spi - ri - tus.

127 Come, Holy Spirit 3

Martin Foster

Come, come, come, Ho - ly Spi - rit.

128 The Song and the Silence

Marty Haugen

Refrain: ALL

Spi - rit of God,   o - pen our hearts   to your song and your si - lence,   dark-ness and light.

Optional choir

Ve - ni,   ve - ni,   Sanc - te   Spi - ri - tus,   Sanc - te   Spi - ri - tus,   ve - ni.

Accompt. 1

Em7/A   A   Em7/A   A
Abm7/Db   Db   Abm7/Db   Db   *simile*

Accompt. 2

Verses set 1

1. You are the Way,   the Gate of sal - va - tion, you are the Door-way of wis - dom and peace.
2. You are the Song   that fills all cre - a - tion, you are the Mu - sic that sounds deep with-in.
3. You are the Word   that rou - ses and frees us, you are the Fire   that set us a - blaze.
4. You are the Love   that binds us to - ge - ther, you are the free-dom that shat - ters all chains.
5. You are the Wind   of God's migh-ty jus - tice, you are the one breath of mer - cy and peace.

Verses set 2

1. Come, O come, great Spi - rit of com-pas - sion. Come, and turn our hearts to you.
2. Let   us each   be Christ to one a - no - ther; hum - ble ser - vants of peace and joy,

3. Come to us,   make us hun - ger for jus - tice. Let us be   one with the low-ly and op-pressed.
4. Let us now   to be one as you taught us; per-fect in love as your chil - dren of light.

Verses set 3

1. Spi - rit of all kind - ness,   spi - rit e - ver mer - ci - ful, Spi - rit of com - pas - sion, grace us with love.
2. Spi - rit of all wis - dom, Spi - rit of in - te - gri - ty, Spi - rit of all in - sight, grace us with light.
3. Spi - rit of all jus - tice, Spi - rit of all right-eous-ness, Spi - rit e - ver faith - ful, teach us your way.

129 Holy Spirit, come to us/Tui amoris ignem

Ostinato Refrain

Ho - ly Spi - rit, come to us, kin - dle in us the fire of your love.
Ve - ni Sanc - te Spi - ri - tus, tu - i a - mo - ris ig - nem ac - cen - de.

Ho - ly Spi - rit, come to us: Ho - ly Spi - rit, come to us.
Ve - ni Sanc - te Spi - ri - tus, Ve - ni, Sanc - te Spi - ri - tus.

Verses

John 15:12

1. Je - sus said, 'I give you a new com - mand - ment: Love one a - no - ther

just as I have loved you.'

2. Je-sus said, 'It is by your love for one a-no-ther

John 13:35

that ev-'ry-one will re-cog-nise you as my dis-ci - ples.

3. Je-sus

John 15:13

said, 'No-one has grea-ter love than this: to lay down one's life for those one loves.'

We know love by this, that Christ laid down his life for us.

1 John 3:16

choose either note

5. This is love: it is not we who have loved God but God who loved us.

1 John 4:10

6. God is love, and those who a - bide in love a - bide in God and God in them.

1 John 4:16

Music by Jacques Berthier (1923-94). © Ateliers et Presses de Taizé

175

130   The Spirit of the Lord

Stephen Dean

The words, from Wisdom 1:7., form the Introit for Pentecost. The chant could be used as a gathering song for that day, with imaginative use of instruments, particularly wind and percussion.

131 Neema, neema

East Africa

Music arrangement © 1995
Geoff Weaver/Jubilate Hymns

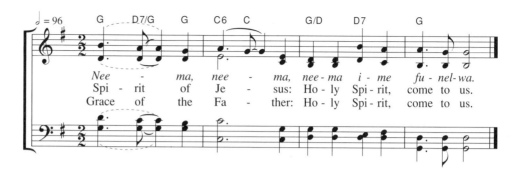

Nee - ma, nee - ma, nee-ma i - me fu-nel-wa.
Spi - rit of Je - sus: Ho - ly Spi - rit, come to us.
Grace of the Fa - ther: Ho - ly Spi - rit, come to us.

132 Into the silence of our hearts (Midday Hymn)

Charles Watson & Ralph Wright

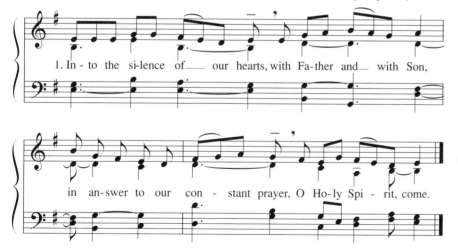

1. In - to the si-lence of___ our hearts, with Fa-ther and___ with Son,

in an-swer to our con - stant prayer, O Ho-ly Spi - rit, come.

2. Then every thought and word of ours
with wonder will inspire,
And all will find in us that love
which you alone my fire.

3. Most holy Father, grant our prayer
through Christ your only Son,
that in your Spirit we may live
and praise you ever One.
Ralph Wright, O.S.B.

This is the hymn *Nunc sancte nobis spiritus*, possibly by St Ambrose (c. 339-397), who introduced hymns to Western christianity. It is part of Midday Prayer, and is included here to create a moment of stillness in the middle of the day. Sing slowly and quietly.

The Lord's Table

Eucharistic Acclamations

133   Trocaire Sanctus

Christopher Willcock

Ostinato Refrain

Ho - san - na, ho - san - na, ho - san - na, ho - san - na. Ho—

Cantors/choir

Ho - ly, ho - ly, ho - ly Lord. God of pow'r and might.

Ho - san - na, ho - san - na, ho - san - na, ho - san - na, ho -
san - na, ho - san - na, ho - san - na, ho - san - na.
Hea - ven and earth are full of-your glo-ry. Ho - san - na, ho -
san - na, ho - san - na, ho - san - na. Bles - sed is
he who comes in the name of the Lord.
Ho - san - na, ho - san - na, ho - san - na, ho - san - na, Ho—-

Ostinato refrain continues ad lib

179

134　Holy, holy (Responsorial Acclamations)

Christopher McCurry

135　Memorial Acclamation

Christ has died, Christ has died, Christ is ris-en, Christ is ris-en, Christ will come a-gain, Christ will come a-gain.

136 Amen

Through him, with him, in him, in the unity of the Ho-ly Spi-rit, all glory and honour are yours, al-migh-ty

Fa-ther, for e - ver and e - ver.

OR

for e-ver and e - ver. A — men, A — men,

A — men, A — men, A — — men. A — — men.

137 Holy, Holy
(Beneath the Tree of Life)

Marty Haugen

138 Memorial Acclamation

Let us proclaim the mystery of faith: Christ has died, Christ has ri - sen, Christ will come a -

gain. Christ has died, Christ has ri - sen, Christ will come a - gain.

139 Doxology and Amen

Through him, with him, in him, in the unity of the Holy Spi - rit, all

Text from the Roman Missal © 1973 International Committee on English in the Liturgy, Inc. Music © 2001 G.I.A. Publications Inc.

*'Alleluia' is not sung in Lent

140 Holy, holy Mass of Hope (Englert)

Eugene Englert

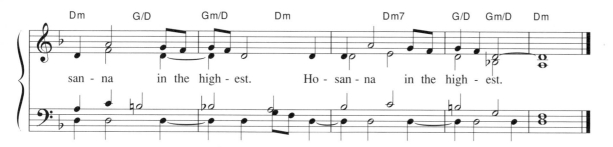

san - na   in the high - est.   Ho - san - na   in the high - est.

141 Memorial Acclamation

Dy - ing you des - troyed our death, ri - sing you re - stored our life. Lord Je - sus, come in glo-ry.

142 Amen

A - men,   a - men,   a - men.

Music © 1998 Eugene Englert

Plainsong, 10th Century

Sanc-tus, sanc-tus, sanc-tus Do - mi - nus De - us Sa - ba - oth. Ple - ni sunt cae - li et

ter - ra glo - ri - a tu - a. Ho - san - na in ex - cel - sis. Be - ne - dic - tus qui

ve - nit in no - mi - ne Do - mi - ni. Ho - san - na in ex - cel - sis.

Accompaniment © 1999 Stephen Dean

144 Amen siakadumisa

South Africa

Anamnesis (Remembering)

145 We remember you

Bernadette Farrell

mem-ber you.   We - re - mem - ber you gave   your   life   for us.   We re -
mem-ber you,   and we thank   you that we   be - long   to you.   We re -

mem - ber.   We be-lieve.   lieve.
mem - ber.   We be-lieve.   lieve.

The Eucharistic Prayer is the centre of
the great rite in which his followers
obey the command of Jesus, *Do this in
memory of me.* This short song could be
sung as an acclamation, a prayer
response, or a meditation, perhaps at a
service of Word and Communion.

Your Kingdom Come

In every Eucharistic rite, between the Great Prayer and the Communion, comes the Lord's Prayer, which in its eight petitions includes everything we are to wish for and to ask God for. Before receiving the Bread of Life it is appropriate to pray for daily bread, and before reaching our closest communion with God and our neighbour we should ask for forgiveness, in the measure in which we ourselves forgive.

In this section are settings of the Lord's Prayer and also pieces which pray for the coming of the Kingdom.

146 Our Father

Laurence Bévenot, O.S.B. (1905-1991)

Our Fa-ther, who art in heav'n, hallowed be thy name; thy kingdom come, thy will be done on earth

as it is in heav'n. Give us this day our dai-ly bread, and for-give us our tres-pas-ses,

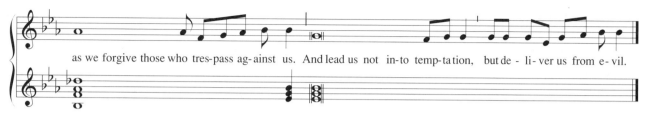

as we forgive those who tres-pass ag-ainst us. And lead us not in-to temp-ta tion, but de - li-ver us from e-vil.

147 Pater Noster

Plainchant

Pa - ter nos - ter, qui es in cae - lis: sanc - ti - fi - ce - tur__

no - men tu - um; ad - ve - ni - at reg num tu - um; fi - at vo - lun - tas tu - a, si - cut in cae - lo,__

et__ in ter - ra. Pa - nem nos - trum co - ti - di - a - num da no - bis ho - di - e;

et di - mit - te no - bis de - bi - ta nos - tra, si - cut et nos di - mit - ti - mus de - bi - to - ri - bus nos - tris;

et ne nos in - du - cas in ten - ta - ti - o - nem, sed li - be - ra nos a ma - lo.

147 Our Father

Barbara Bridge

149 Mayenziwe (Your will be done)

South Africa

English text: Your will be done on earth, O Lord.

150 Lord's Prayer Litany

Janet Lunt

Opening *Slow and reflective*

Lord, hear our prayer.

Refrain *sung between spoken prayers, and could incorporate the opening*

Your king - dom come, your will be

done on earth as it is in hea - ven.

Prayer Section *Optional: for humming or playing beneath prayers*

Optional Ending *for festival occaions, especially Christmas*

Glo-ry be to God in the high-est heav'n and on earth his peace to all!

151 Your kingdom come, O Lord

Nicolai Zabolotski

Your king-dom come, O Lord. Your king-dom come, O Lord. Your king-dom come, O Lord. Your king-dom come, O Lord.

152 The will of your love

Suzanne Toolan, R.S.M.

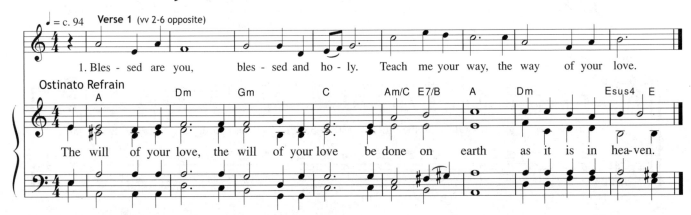

Verse 1 (vv 2-6 opposite)

1. Bles - sed are you, bles - sed and ho - ly. Teach me your way, the way of your love.

Ostinato Refrain

The will of your love, the will of your love be done on earth as it is in hea-ven.

2. O - pen my eyes__ that I may know your won-ders, the won-ders of your way, the won-ders of your love.

3. O__ God, teach me wis-dom; O__ God, the wis-dom of your love.

4. A lamp to my feet, a light to my path is your word, your word__ of truth.

5. Hap-py are you who fol-low the path of your God, who live in God's love as it is in hea-ven.

6. Hap-py are you who walk in truth; in you there is no dark ness, in you there is light.

The peace of Christ

In the Roman Rite the last acts before communion are the sign of peace, followed by the Lamb of God (Agnus Dei) with its final petition *Grant us peace*. This section includes settings of the Lamb of God and songs and chants concerned with Peace.

153 Peace Prayer

Christopher Willcock

Lord Je-sus Christ, you said to your a-

pos-tles: '! leave you peace, my peace I give you.' Look not___ on our

Text from the Roman Missal © 1973 International Committee on English in the Liturgy, Inc. Music © Christopher Willcock

203

154 My peace I leave you

Taizé

My peace I leave you, my peace I give you:
trou-ble not your hearts. My peace I leave you, my peace I give you: Be not a-fraid.

Music by Jacques Berthier (1923-94) © Ateliers et Presses de Taizé

155 Give peace in our time

Martin Foster

Ostinato Refrain

Give peace in our time, O Lord. in our

hearts, in our homes, in our land, in our world. Give peace in our time, O Lord. Give

When singing verses
Cantor: 'A' below

Cantor: 'B' below

Lord. ah_____ Give peace in our time, O Lord. ah_____ Give

Optional Verses (Cantor) A

B

Stems down: vv. 1, 6

1. May the Church— pro-claim your gos-pel   to the poor— and the op— pressed.
2. For— na-tions— torn by con-flict.   for— coun-tries— bro-ken by ha-tred.
3. For— peo-ple— starv-ing for food;—   for— peo-ple— thirst-ing for life.—
4. For— all— scarred by a-buse;—   for— all— hurt by ad-dic-tion.—
5. For— all— wait-ing for news;—   for— all— bur-dened by sin.—
6. In the light of your re-sur-rec-tion;   in the hope— of each new day.—

156 Peace be with you (Na Jijoho)

from Benin
arr. Geoff Weaver

This song is very popular in Benin, and is sung for thanksgiving and many other occasions.

157 Da pacem cordium

Taizé

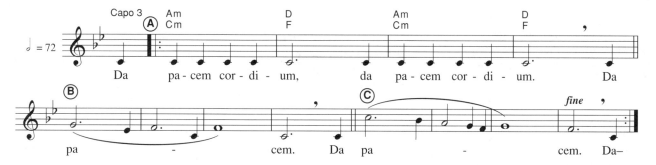

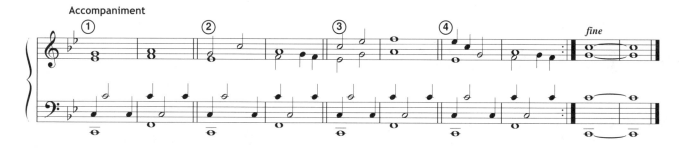

This chant was formerly *Da pacem, Domine* (Give peace, O Lord.) If you want to sing it in English, use the wording:

Give peace to eve-ry heart; give peace to eve-ry heart. Give peace, Lord. Give peace, Lord.

Music by Jacques Berthier © Ateliers et Presses de Taizé

158   Prayer of St Francis

Christopher Walker

Solo verses 1-10

1. Where there is ha - tred, let us sow love.
2. Where there is dis - cord, let us bring par - don.
3. Where there is doubt, let us sow faith.
4. Where there is er - ror, let us sow truth.
5. Where there's des - pair, let us bring hope.
6. Where there is sad - ness, let us bring joy.
7. Where there is dark - ness, let us shine light.
8. Let us not seek to be con - soled, but to con - sole.
9. Nor to be un - der-stood, but to un - der - stand.
10. Nor to be loved, but to love with all our heart.

159 Dona nobis pacem

Traditional

① Do - na no - bis pa - cem, pa-cem; do - na no - bis pa - cem.

② Do - na no - bis pa - cem, do - na no - bis pa - cem.

③ Do - na no - bis pa - cem, do - na no - bis pa - cem.

The Breaking of Bread and Communion

**160
Agnus
Dei XVIII**

Plainsong,
10th Century

Ag-nus De - i, qui tol-lis pec - ca - ta mun-di, mi-se-re-re no - bis.

Ag-nus De - i, qui tol-lis pec - ca - ta mun-di, mi-se-re-re no - bis.

Ag-nus De - i, qui tol-lis pec - ca - ta mun-di, do-na no-bis pa - cem.

161 Lamb of God 1

Martin Foster

Je-sus, Lamb of God, you take a-way the sin of the world; have mer-cy on us. world; grant us peace.

This setting is easily adapted to a Responsorial format, in which the cantor sings the whole phrase and everyone repeats 'have mercy on us' or 'grant us peace.'

Other verses

Jesus, Prince of Peace,
Jesus, Bread of Life,
Jesus, cup of love,
Jesus, Word made flesh,

Jesus, risen Lord,
Jesus, Paschal Lamb,

162 Lamb of God 2

Stephen Dean

* Lamb of God may be replaced by other suitable phrases: Bread of Life... Prince of Peace... etc (see nos. 161 and 163)

Marty Haugen

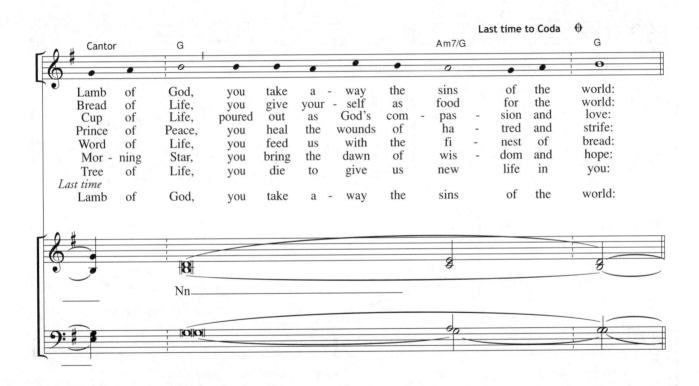

Like the Eucharistic Acclamations (138-140), this is taken from the Mass setting *Beneath the Tree of Life* (GIA G-5221).

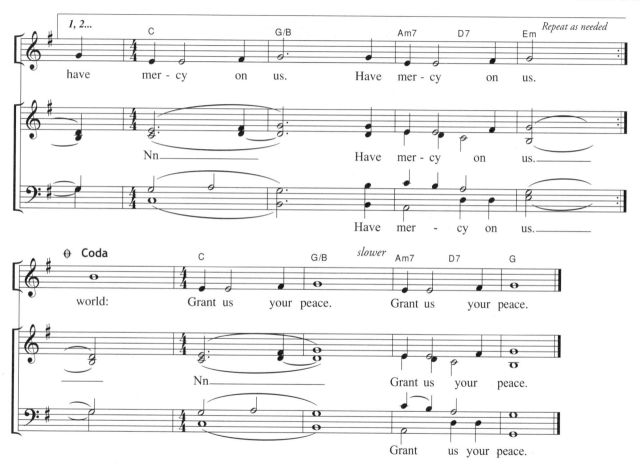

Communion

164   Draw near to the Lord

Philip Jakob

Draw near to the Lord and his light will shine up - on you. Taste and see that the Lord is good.

Draw near to the Lord and his light will shine up - on you. taste and see that the Lord is good.

Psalm 34, from which these words are taken, has been sung at Communion since very early times.
Notice the quote from the 'Dresden Amen' which Wagner uses in *Parsifal* whenever there is mention of the Holy Grail.

165 This is the body of Christ

John L. Bell

This is the bo - dy of Christ,

bro - ken that we may be whole; this cup as pro - mised by God,

true to his word, cra - dles our Lord: food for the good of the soul.

166 Bread of life from heaven

Argentinian
arr. Marty Haugen

Text by Susan Briehl

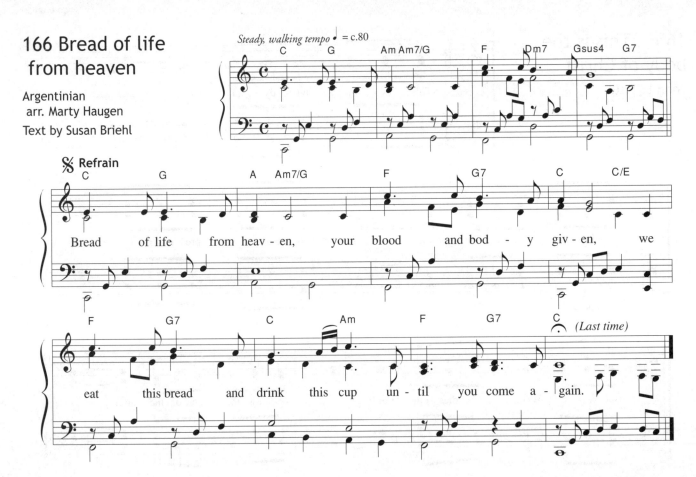

1. Break now the bread of Christ's sac-ri-fice; Giv-ing thanks, hun-gry ones gath-er round.
2. Seek not the food that will pass a-way; Set your hearts on the food that en-dures.
3. Love as the One who, in love for you, gave him self for the life of the world.
4. Take in the light that will nev-er dim, Taste the life that is strong-er than death.
5. Dwell in the One who now dwells in you; Make your home in the life-giv-ing Word.
6. Drink of this cup and de-clare his death; Eat this bread and be-lieve Eas-ter morn.

G   G7/B   C   C/E   F   F/A   G/B   C

Eat all of you, and be sat-is-fied; in Christ's pres-ence the loaves will a-bound.
Come, learn the true and the liv-ing way, that the full-ness of life may be yours.
Live in the One who is food for you, that your hun-ger and thirst be no more.
Live in the One who will come, and then raise you up at the last with the blest.
Know on-ly Christ, Ho-ly One of God, and be-lieve in the truth you have heard.
Trust his re-turn and, with ev-'ry breath praise the One in whom you are re-born.

poco rit   D.S

Bm7   E7   Am   Am7/G   D/F#   D7   Gsus4   G7

219

167 Jesus, you are the bread

Bernadette Farrell

Refrain

Je - sus, you are the bread we long for.

Je - sus, you are the word we need._____ Je - sus, here in your

ga - thered peo - ple to - day, you live to___ show us the way._____

220

Verses Cantor

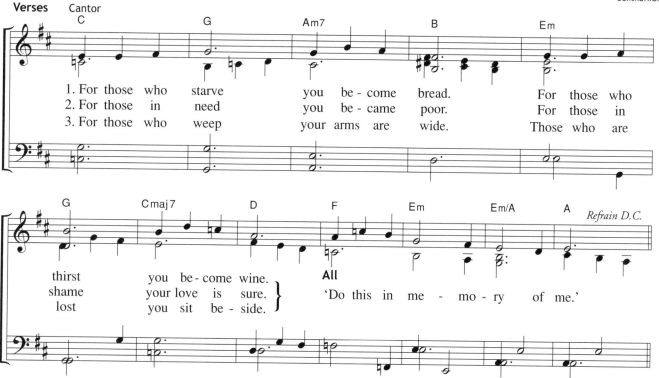

1. For those who starve you be-come bread. For those who
2. For those in need you be-came poor. For those in
3. For those who weep your arms are wide. Those who are

thirst you be-come wine.
shame your love is sure. }
lost you sit be-side. }

All
'Do this in me - mo - ry of me.'

Refrain D.C.

4. For those alone you speak your word,
   For those oppressed your cry is heard:
   'Do this in memory of me.'

5. King of all kings, choosing to serve.
   To the world's eyes failed and absurd.
   'Do this in memory of me.'

168 Amen, amen, it shall be so

Martin Foster

Al-le-lu - ia, al-le-lu - ia. A-men, A - men.

1. Christ is
2. Christ died
3. In
4. In
5. Christ is

A - men, a - men, so shall it be. A–

D   Em/D   A4   A   D

Refrain as a Profession of Faith: see p.102

This may be sung in refrain-verse-refrain form, finishing as an ostinato (refrain only.) This will allow the cantor (if there is only one) to receive communion.

ri - sen from the dead,_____ and__ brings_____ new life._____
once_____ for our sins,_____ so that we_____ have life._____
Christ_____ we have died_____ so we rise_____ with him._____
Christ_____ we be - come_____ a__ new_____ cre - a - tion.
ri - sen in__ glo - ry at the Fa - ther's right hand.

Chords: G C G/B A D/F# A D *D.C.*

6. Christ, the light for the world
   that will never die
7. Through word and water we rise
   in Christ.
8. In the waters of life we rise
   with Christ.
9. Through oil we are sealed by
   God's Spirit of grace.
10. We proclaim our faith, the
    faith of the Church.

11. At the feast of the Lamb all shall be fed.
12. First fruits of milk and honey flow.
13. At this table we welcome new members with joy.
14. At this table we will share Christ's body and blood.
15. Our food for the journey to become like Christ.

16. As we eat this bread we become Christ's body.
17. The body of Christ for a broken world
18. We will share our bread with this broken world.
19. Broken bread for the poor; the body of Christ.
20. With the stranger, with the outcast, we will share our lives.

21. As we drink this cup we become Christ's lifeblood.
22. The blood of Christ poured out in love.
23. The blood of Christ for a broken world.
24. We will share Christ's love with a broken world.
25. Through his body and blood we can share Christ's love.

26. With all who are thirsting we will share Christ's love.
27. With all who are hungry we will break our bread.
28. With all who are lonely we will greet as Christ.
29. With all who are angry we will share Christ's peace.

30. All those who are hurt ing will be healed in Christ.
31. All those who are naked will be clothed in Christ.
32. All those who cry out will be heard as Christ.
33. All those who are captive will be freed in Christ.

34. When we eat this bread and drink this cup.
35. We proclaim your death and resurrection.
36. Until you come in glory, Lord.
37. Amen, amen, so shall it be:
38. Alleluia, alleluia.

© 2004 Martin Foster

169 Taste and see (Psalm 34)

Anne Ward

Cantor (verses ad lib.)

1. I bless the Lord in ev-'ry place and time,
2. Now join with me and glo-ri-fy the Lord.
3. Look on the Lord and let him shine on you;

Taste and see the good-ness of the Lord.

In praise of God I shall lift up my voice my soul shall make its
To-ge-ther let us praise God's migh-ty name. I sought the Lord and
let not your face be hid-den, turned a-way. The poor cry out, and

Taste and see the good-ness of the Lord. Bles-sed are they who

boast in God a-lone. hear him, all hum-ble peo-ple,___ and re-joice.
he has an-swered me; and set me free from all my___ fear and shame
God will heed their call, and res-cue them from trou-ble ev-'ry day.

hope in God. Taste and see the Lord is good in-deed.

224

3. Look on the Lord and let him shine on you;
   let not your face be hidden, turned away.
   The poor cry out, and God will heed their call,
   and rescue them from trouble every day.

4. The Lord has set an angel close at hand,
   to keep his faithful people free from harm.
   O taste and see that the Lord is good,
   and put your trust in God's almighty arm.

5. Let not your mouth be full of evil words,
   and keep your tongue from spreading lies abroad,
   When evil ways attract you, turn aside,
   seek peace and strive to walk beside the Lord.

The verses are a later addition to
the ostinato refrain of this
Communion processional. There
are instrumental parts, which may
be found in Decani edition 0278.

Choir (Melody in alto) choir and keyboard

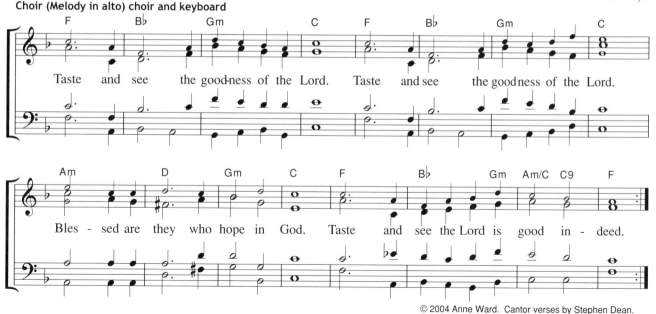

Taste and see the goodness of the Lord. Taste and see the goodness of the Lord.

Bles - sed are they who hope in God. Taste and see the Lord is good in - deed.

170 Shoulder my yoke

Anne Ward

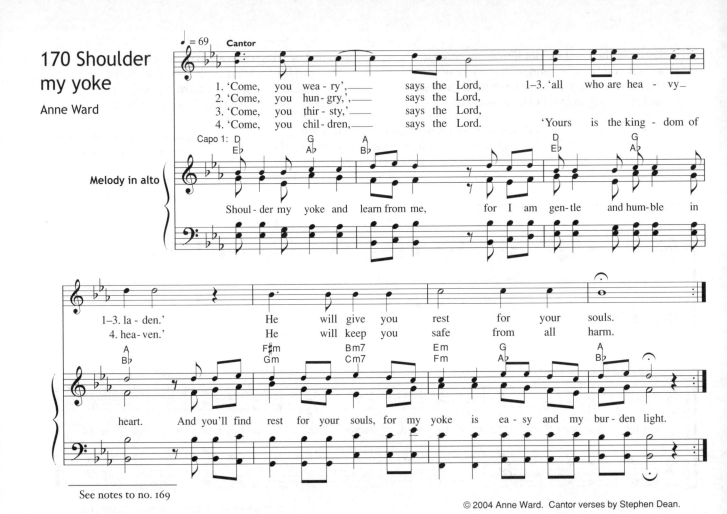

Melody in alto

1. 'Come, you wea - ry', ——— says the Lord,
2. 'Come, you hun - gry,', ——— says the Lord,
3. 'Come, you thir - sty,' ——— says the Lord,
4. 'Come, you chil - dren, ——— says the Lord.

1–3. 'all who are hea - vy—
'Yours is the king - dom of

Shoul - der my yoke and learn from me, for I am gen - tle and hum - ble in

1–3. la - den.'
4. hea - ven.'

He will give you rest for your souls.
He will keep you rest safe from all harm.

heart. And you'll find rest for your souls, for my yoke is ea - sy and my bur - den light.

See notes to no. 169

171   Not on bread alone

Stephen Dean

1. Taste and see; taste and see; taste and see that the Lord is good.
2. I will praise the Lord all my days; praise of God e-ver on my lips.
3. Lord, you are the Saviour of the world; give us li-ving wa-ter to quench our thirst.
4. Lord, you are the light of the world, ligh-ten our way on the path of life.
5. Lord, you are re-sur-rec-tion and life, those who be-lieve have e-ter-nal life.
6. Turn to the Lord with all your heart, God of com-pas-sion and ten-der love.

Ostinato Refrain

Not on bread a-lone are we nou-rished, but on ev-ery word from the mouth of God.

172 Holy Manna

Shaker tune
'Love is little',
arr. Steven Warner

Text and music arrangement ©
1999 World Library Publications

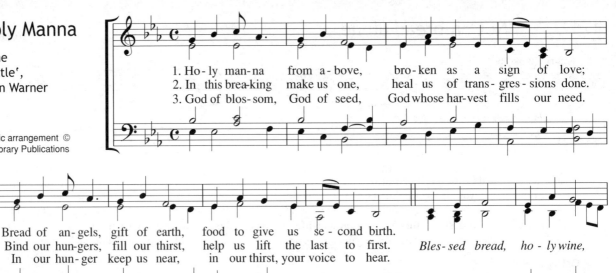

1. Ho- ly man- na from a- bove, bro- ken as a sign of love;
2. In this brea- king make us one, heal us of trans- gres- sions done.
3. God of blos- som, God of seed, God whose har- vest fills our need.

Bread of an- gels, gift of earth, food to give us se- cond birth.
Bind our hun- gers, fill our thirst, help us lift the last to first. *Bles- sed bread, ho- ly wine,*
In our hun- ger keep us near, in our thirst, your voice to hear.

feed us with this sa- cred sign. Bles- sed bread, ho- ly wine, feed us with this sa- cred sign.

The text is by Steven Warner. His arrangement for SAB voices, C and B♭ instruments is in World Library Pubs. edition 7246

173 Always in your presence

Philip Jakob

O— Lord, we are al-ways in your pre-sence— In
pre — sence

you we live and move and have our be-ing— You hold— us— in the
be - ing.

palm— of your hand and you lead us to your glo-ry.— O—

A fuller version
with verses from
Psalm 72 may be
found in Decani
edition 0217

229

Giving thanks

174 Give thanks with a joyful heart

Henry Smith
arranged by David Peacock

unhurried

Give thanks with a joy-ful heart, give thanks to the Ho-ly One, give thanks_____ be-cause He's gi-ven Je-sus Christ,_____ your Son. Give Son. And

Words and music © 1978 Integrity's Hosanna! Music, administered by Kingsway's Thankyou Music, PO Box 75, Eastbourne, E. Sussex BN23 6NW, UK for the UK only. Used with permission.

175 We thank you Jesus

Tanzanian,
arr. Geoff Weaver

Ah - san - te Ye - su, a - min, Ah - san - te Ye - su, a -
We thank you, Je - sus; a - men, we thank you, Je - sus; a -

min, Ah - san - te Ye - su, a - min. Hal - le - lu - jah! A - min.
men, we thank you, Je - sus; a - men. Hal - le - lu - jah! A - men.

176 Glory and gratitude and praise

John L. Bell

firmly

Glo - ry and gra - ti - tude and praise now let earth to

Glo - ry ____ and gra - ti -

hea - ven raise. Glo - ry and gra - ti - tude and praise: these we of - fer to God.___

tude___ and praise___ these we of - fer to God.

Grace before meals

177
Now bless, Lord, the bread

Federico Pagura

Ben - di - ce, Se - nor, nues - tro pan, y da pan a los que tien - en
Now bless, Lord, the bread you have giv'n; and give bread to this our world that is

ham - bre, y ham - bre de jus - ti - cia_a los que tien - en pan. Ben - di - ce, Se - nor, nues - tro pan.
hun - gry; to those with bread give hun - ger for true jus - tice now! And bless, Lord, the bread that we share.

178
Magnificat 1

Stephen Dean/
The Grail

Refrain ♩ = c. 152

The Lord has done great things for me: Ho-ly is his name, ho-ly is his name.

Cantor *slower* ♩ = c. 126

My soul glo-ri-fies the Lord: my spi-rit re-joi-ces in God my Sa-viour. 2. He

ALL

looks on his ser-vant in her low-li-ness; hence-forth all a-ges shall call me bles-sed. THE

D.S.

Cantor *freely*

3. The Almighty works mar-vels for me: Holy his name. *to v. 4*
5. He puts forth his arm in strength, and scatters the proud-hearted. *to v. 6*

234

4. His mercy is from age to age on those who fear him. *to v. 5*
6. He casts the migh-ty from their thrones, and rai-ses the low-ly. THE

7. He fills the star-ving with good things, sends the rich a-way empty. 8. He pro-tects Is-ra-el his servant, re-memb'ring his

mer-cy. 9. The mer-cy pro-mised to our fa-thers, to A-bra-ham and his child-ren for e-ver. THE

10. Give praise to the Fa - ther Al - migh - ty; to Je - sus Christ, his Son, our Sa - viour.

ALL

Response D.S.

11. Give praise to the Spi - rit e - ver - las - ting, to God who reigns on high for e - ver. THE

179 Magnificat 2

Peter Warlock (1894-1930)
Words by Martin Foster

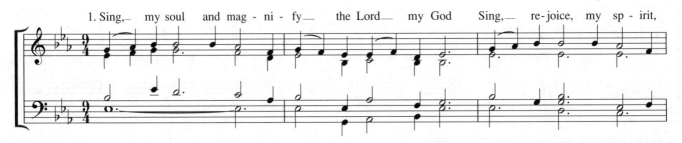

1. Sing,— my soul and mag - ni - fy— the Lord— my God Sing,— re - joice, my sp - irit,

God— has come— to save. He— looks down on me,— his ser - vant, hum-ble of heart

From— this mo - ment all— to come— will call— me blest.

Text © 2004 Martin Foster.
Harmony by Stephen Dean.

2. God the mighty, God the holy cares for me;
Cares for all who fear and bless his holy name;
God the strong will rout the proud in their conceit.
Thrones are toppled, yet the poor are lifted up.

3. All who hunger will be fed by God's own hand.
All the rich are empty-handed in God's plan.
He protects with love and mercy Israel:
mercy promised; love remembered for all time.

4. Glory sing to God the Father, mighty Lord,
Glory sing to God the Son, the Word made flesh.
Glory sing to God the Spirit, gift of grace.
All God's people, though all ages praise your God.

Luke 1:46-55, versified by Martin Foster

This tune comes from Peter Warlock's *Capriol Suite*, where it is called *Pieds en l'air*. It was developed by him from a phrase of a Breton dance found in the *Orchésographie* (1589) by Thoinot Arbeau, a book which has also given us the tune for *Ding dong merrily on high*.

180
Magnificat 3

Taizé

The Almighty has done great things for me:
   holy is his name.

His mercy stretches from age to age
   upon those who revere him.

He has put forth his arm in strength
   scattering the proud-hearted.

He has cast down the mighty from their
   thrones
   and lifted up the lowly.

He has filled the hungry with good things,
   and send the rich away empty-handed.

He has helped his servant Israel
   ever remembering his love,

the love he promised to our ancestors,
   to Abraham and his children for
   ever.

Following the Lord

After giving thanks for what we have received, Word and Eucharist, we are strengthened for service and closer to the Lord who gives such gifts. This section includes songs in which we acknowledge our dependence and ask for help to lead a life dedicated to love of God and love of others.

181 This is my commandment

Traditional

This is my com-mand-ment, that you love one an-oth-er that your joy may be full.

This is my com-mand-ment, that you love one an-oth-er that your joy may be full, that your

joy may be full, that your joy may be full. This is my com-mand-ment, that you

love one an-oth-er that your joy may be full.

182   Jesu tawa pano (Jesus, we are here)

Patrick Matzikenyiri

Jesus, we are here,
we are here for you.

Other verses could be added:
  we are here *with* you.
  we are here *in* you.

This song, which would also serve as a Gathering song, may be sung in Shona or English. The last line of the English version is fitted as shown under the stave.

183 Open our eyes

Angela Reith

O - pen our eyes___ to see. O - pen our ears___ to hear.

O - pen our life___ to live your cal - ling, o - pen us, Lord, ___ to love.*

184 Jesus, Saviour (Psalm 25)

Martin Foster

The refrain and verses opposite form an Advent gathering song (for the full version see Decani edition 0273)

**Verses from
Psalm 25**

1. Lord, make me know your ways,— Lord, teach me your
2. Re - mem - ber your mer - cy, Lord, and the love you have shown from of
3. The Lord is good and up - right, shows the path to those who
4. To the Fa - ther al - migh-ty give praise to his Son, Je - sus Christ the

paths. Make me walk in your truth and teach me, for you are God my Saviour.
old. Do not re - mem - ber the sins of my youth, in your love re - mem - ber me.
stray, - guides the hum - ble in the right path, and tea - ches the way to the poor.
Lord To the Spir - it who dwells in our hearts, both now and for e - ver, A - men. -

**184a
Longing, Trusting**
Advent Verses

1. Stay a - wake for the Lord is near. Stay a - wake, be on your
2. Pre - pare a way for the Lord Make a path straight through the
3. Re - joice in the Lord who is near shout for joy, all those who
4. The Lord will come to save; come in power and come in

guard. The day of the Lord is at hand: for our God has come to save.
de - sert. Raise up val - leys, lay the hills low for our God has come to save.
wait. For the Lord is a - mong his peo-ple, for our God has come to save.
glo - ry. Bringing peace and jus - tice for all, Come, O Lord, do not de - lay!

Gm   C/E   F   Gm   A4   A   Dm

243

185 If you would be my disciples

Christopher Walker

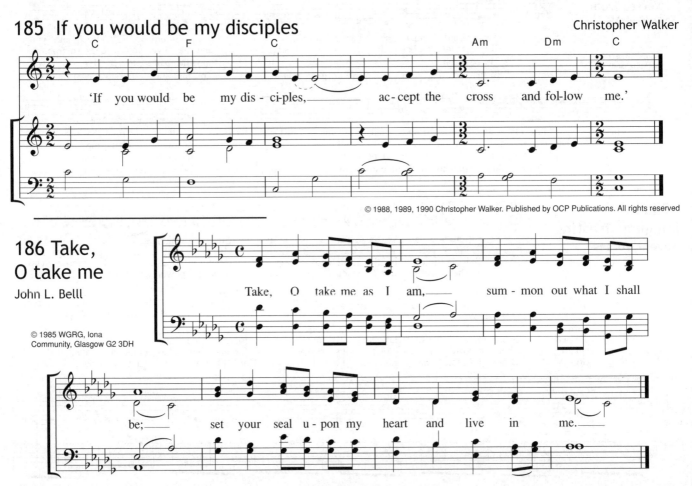

'If you would be my dis-ci-ples,_____ ac-cept the cross and fol-low me.'

186 Take, O take me

John L. Belll

Take, O take me as I am,_____ sum-mon out what I shall be;_____ set your seal u-pon my heart and live in me._____

244

186a Psalm 40

Stephen Dean/The Grail

These verses may be
sung with the previous
chant as a response.

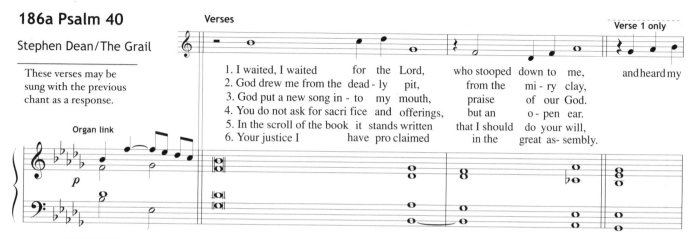

Verses

Verse 1 only

1. I waited, I waited   for the Lord,   who stooped down to me,   and heard my
2. God drew me from the dead - ly   pit,   from the   mi - ry   clay,
3. God put a new song in - to   my   mouth,   praise   of   our   God.
4. You do not ask for sacri fice   and   offerings,   but an   o - pen   ear.
5. In the scroll of the book   it   stands written   that I should   do your will,
6. Your justice I   have pro claimed   in the   great as- sembly.

Organ link

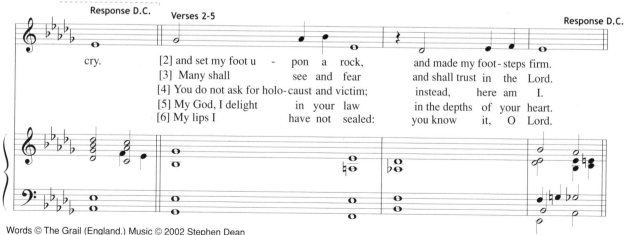

Response D.C.   **Verses 2-5**   **Response D.C.**

cry.   [2] and set my foot u - pon   a rock,   and made my foot- steps firm.
[3] Many shall   see and fear   and shall trust in   the   Lord.
[4] You do not ask for holo- caust and victim;   instead,   here am   I.
[5] My God, I delight   in your law   in the depths of your heart.
[6] My lips I   have not   sealed: you know   it,   O   Lord.

Words © The Grail (England.) Music © 2002 Stephen Dean

187 I'll follow my Lord

I'll fol-low my Lord, I'll fol-low my Lord, I'll fol-low my Lord to Je-sus I cling;
Kay Yah-weh a - ko, kay Yah-weh a-ko, Kay Yah-weh a - ko, ma - na - na - na - gan.

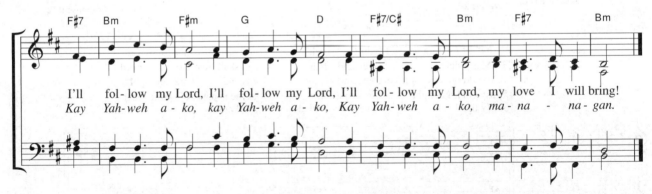

I'll fol-low my Lord, I'll fol-low my Lord, I'll fol-low my Lord, my love I will bring!
Kay Yah-weh a - ko, kay Yah-weh a-ko, Kay Yah-weh a - ko, ma - na - na - gan.

Words: from the Tagalog. English words © 1993 in this version Words & Music/Jubilate Music.
Music: unknown, arranged Geoff Weaver. Music arrangement © 1993 Geoff Weaver/Jubilate Music

188 All that I think or say

Christopher Walker

189   In life and death

Marty Haugen

In life and death, we are yours, O God, in life and death, we are yours.

One of three Litanies of Healing (GIA G-3607) . Written or improvised
prayers may be used, or the verses opposite sung, or a combination

*Play these two bars ad lib as intro under spoken
introduction and during spoken prayers.*

248

To sung verses

Verses (Cantor) * *The verses are sung instead of (or as well as) spoken prayers.*

yours.

1. Just as Christ has been raised from the dead, so we might
2. All the suff - 'ring we now must en- dure, does not might com-
3. So we live no lon- ger for our selves, we live and

D.S. **Coda**

walk in the new- ness of life.
pare with the glo - ry to come.
die in the pro- mise of Christ.

yours.

190 The face of Christ

Bernadette Farrell

Verses

1. But when, Lord?
   When did we see you hungry
     and give you food to eat?
   When did we see you, Lord?

2. But when, Lord?
   When did we see you thirsty
     and give you water to drink?
   When did we see you, Lord?

3. But when, Lord?
   When did we see you a stranger
     and welcome you in?
   When did we see you, Lord?

4. But when, Lord?
   When did we see you naked
     and give you clothes to wear?
   When did we see you, Lord?

5. But when, Lord?
   When did we see you ill
     and come to sit at your bedside?
   When did we see you, Lord?

6. But when, Lord?
   When did we see you in prison
     and come to visit you?
   When did we see you, Lord?

7. But when, Lord?
   When did we see you - the Christ,
     the Son of Mary, our brother, our God?
   When did we see you, Lord?

The response is intended to be sung by all, unaccompanied, SATB, though keyboard may be used as well. The interlude can be played softly underthe spoken word. Two ways (of many) in which this piece can be used are:

1) Prophetic Voices: contemporary icons are held up (figures such as Oscar Romero or Desmond Tutu.) A sentence or two from their writings is spoken, and the response sung. The icon is placed centrally during the singing.

2) Images of God: pictures of ordinary people (slides or just images) are shown and scripture proclaimed before each response.

191 Saranam

Words by D.T.Niles
Punjabi melody,
arr. Geoff Weaver

Words © after D.T.Niles, revised by permission/
Christian Conference of Asia.
Music arr.© 1995 Geoff Weaver/Jubilee Hymns

Sa - ra - nam, sa - ra - nam, sa - ra - nam,

Je - sus, Sav - iour, Lord, now to you I come, Sa - ra nam, sa - ra - nam, sa - ra - nam;

you my Rock, my re - fuge, my heav'n - ly home, Sa - ra - nam, sa - ra - nam, sa - ra - nam.

1. From the earth wher-ev-er I may be, out of des - pe - ra - tion and through
2. In your heart give me a hid - ing place, and be-neath your wings let me find

a - go - ny, I cry in help-less-ness - O ans - wer me, *Sa-ra-nam, sa-ra-nam, sa-ra-nam.*
shel - tering grace; O let me see the sun-shine of your face,

3. Then with joy to you my vows I'll pay,
   and give thanks for all your mercy every day;
   I'll humbly follow in your perfect way,
   Saranam, saranam, saranam.
      Jesus, Saviour ...

4. Glory to the Father and the Son,
   with the Holy Spirit ever Three-in-One;
   we'll sing in heaven praises here begun,
   Saranam, saranam, saranam.
      Jesus, Saviour ...

A much loved hymn from the Indian subcontinent. *Saranam* means 'refuge' or 'I take refuge.'

192 Bambelela

The song was heard in South Africa by Mairi Munro and Martine Stemerick at the JL Zwane Memorial Congregation in Gugulethu, Capetown, South Africa, led by the choir leader, Leonorah Kunene. It was being sung as a response to the tesimony of a woman whose son had died of AIDS. 'Bambelela' is a Xhosa word that translates 'hold on', in the sense of hopeful perseverance. In the first setting the leader may use different phrase to introduce repeats, e.g. 'In times of sorrow', 'In times of trouble' or 'When you are alone.' All royalties from this song go to support the work of the JL Zwane Memorial Congregation.

193 You will show me the path of life

Scott Soper

Cue notes, Verses only

256

you there can be no good.
Lord at my side I shall stand firm.

Verse 3

3. My heart ex-ults, my
spi-rit sings, e-ven my bo-dy trusts in you; for you will not a-ban-don my
soul to death, nor let me sink in-to the grave.

This is a setting of Psalm 16:1-2. 7-9, with verse 11 as the response. This psalm occurs in the Roman Lectionary at the Easter Vigil and several liturgies of the Easter Season. It may be used as a responsorial or communion psalm.

194 Over my head

Spiritual

O-ver my head   I hear mu-sic in the air.   O-ver my head

I hear mu-sic   in the air.   O-ver my head   I hear mu-sic   in the air,

Verses

1. O   when the world is   si - lent____
2. And   when I'm fee - ling lone - ly____
3. Now when I think on   Je - sus____

there must be   a God some - where.   I hear

O when the world is si-lent — O
And when I'm fee-ling lone-ly — And
Now when I think on Je-sus — Now

mu-sic in the air. — I hear mu-sic in the air.

when the world is si-lent —
when I'm fee-ling lone-ly —
when I think on Je-sus —

I hear mu-sic in the air, — there must be a God some-where.

African-American traditional. Arrangement by John L. Bell, © 2002 WGRG, Iona Community, Glasgow G2 3DH

259

195 Send down the fire

Marty Haugen

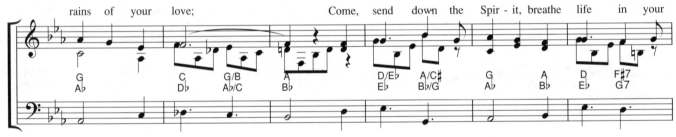

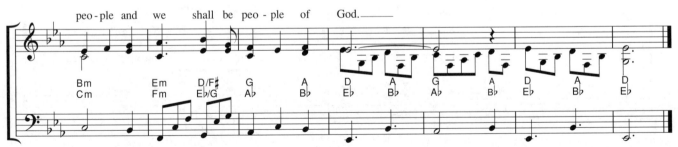

From *Tales of Wonder*, also available as an octavo, GIA edition no. 3915

1. Call us to be your com-pas-sion,___ teach us the song of your
2. Call us to wit-ness your King-dom,___ give us the pre-sence of

love;___ Give us hearts that sing, give us deeds that ring, make us
Christ,___ May your ho-ly light keep us shi-ning bright, ev-er

ring with the song of your love.___
shine with the pre-sence of Christ.___

3
Call us to learn of your mercy,
teach us the way of your peace;
Give us hearts that feel,
give us hands that heal,
make us walk in the way of your peace.

4
Call us to witness your kingdom,
give us the presence of Christ;
May your holy light
keep us shining bright,
ever shine with the presence of Christ.

261

196 Alleluia! Raise the Gospel

Bernadette Farrell

Verses

1. Bles - sed those whose hearts are gen - tle. Bles - sed those whose spi-rits are strong.
2. Bles - sed those who work for jus - tice. Bles - sed those who an-swer the call.
3. Trem - ble, you who build up ri - ches. Trem - ble, you with o - pu-lent lives.

Bles - sed those who choose to bring forth right where there is wrong.
Bles - sed those who dare to dream of las - ting peace for all.
Trem - ble, when you meet the poor and see Christ in their eyes.

4. Tremble, you who thirst for power.
Tremble, you who live for acclaim.
Tremble, when you find no comfort
in your wealth and fame.

5. Glory like the stars of heaven,
glory like the sun in the sky.
Glory shines upon all people
equal in God's eyes.

6. Glory to the Word of Justice.
Glory to the Spirit of Peace.
Glory to the God of love
whose blessings never cease.

Blessing and going forth

'But be doers of the word, and not merely hearers' (James 1:23). After hearing the word and coming to be fed at the table of the Lord, in short, after learning the lesson of service to others, we must resolve to go out and do likewise.
See also nos. 6 and 14, Gathering Songs which also include verses for concluding worship.

197 Now go in peace

Caribbean

Now go in peace, now go in love, from the Fa-ther a-bove

Je-sus Christ the Son stay with you till the day is done.

Ho-ly Spi-rit en-cir-cle you in all you think and do.

Once a-gain, God's bless-ing be with us. A-men. Now go in

This round was collected from a second-generation Caribbean family living in Coventry. It could be sung in unison two or three times before starting the round.

198 We will walk with God

Swaziland

We will walk with God, my bro-thers, we will walk with God.
Si - zo-ham - ba-na ye wo, wo, wo, si - zo-ham - ba na-ye.

We will go re - joi - cing till the king - dom has come.
Ngomhla wen-ja bu-la, si - zo-ham - ba na ye.

We will go re - joi - cing till the king - dom has come.
Ngom-hla wen-ja - bu-la, si - zo-ham - ba na ye.

Alternative words

1
We are on the Lord's road, wo, wo, wo
we are on the Lord's road *(repeat)*
On our way to heaven,
we are on the Lord's road. *(repeat)*

2
We shall sing the Lord's praise...
On our way to heaven,
we shall sing the Lord's praise...

3
We shall live the Lord's word...
On our way to heaven,
we shall live the Lord's worde...

4
Hallelujah, Amen...

South African

Original words and music transcribed by the Swedish Youth Exchange Project *Meeting Swaziland.* Translation by John L. Bell, © 2002 WGRG, Iona Community, Glasgow G2 3DH

199 Go in peace

John Schiavone

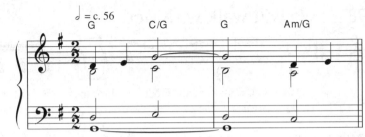

𝄋 1st time Cantor, all repeat

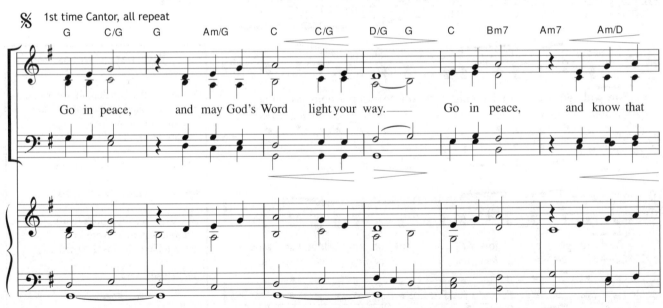

Go in peace, and may God's Word light your way. Go in peace, and know that

200 Go out to the whole world (Ps 117)

Philp Jakob

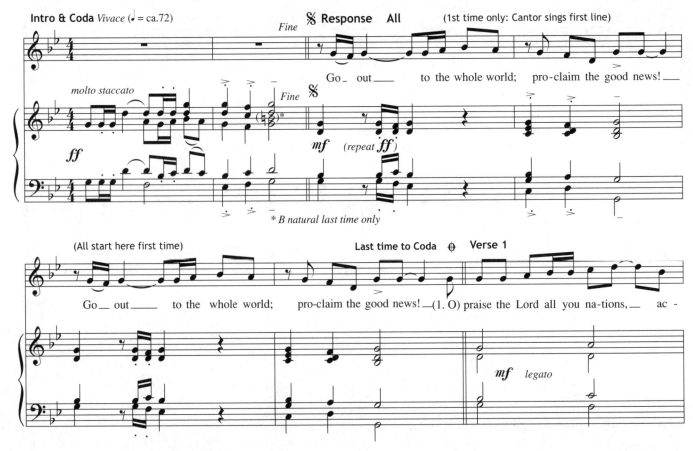

D.S.

claim God, all you peo-ples. __ O praise the Lord all you na-tions, __ ac-claim God, all you peo-ples. __

Verse 2

D.S. al Coda

2. Strong is God's love for us; the Lord is faith-ful for e-ver. __ Strong is God's love for us; the Lord is faith-ful for e-ver. __

mf *legato*

This psalm is sung as a Responsorial Psalm on certain Sundays in Ordinary Time, and at ordinations. A fuiller version is in OCP edition 11945

Text © 1993 The Grail (England.) Music © 1996, 2002 Philip Jakob

269

201 Christ is the morning star

Philip Jakob, words by St Bede

Christ is the mor - ning star, who when the night of this world is past,

brings to his saints the pro-mise of the light of life and o-pens ev - er-last-ing day.

Christ is the mor - ning star, who when the night of this world is past,

brings to his saints the pro-mise of the light of life and o-pens ev-er-last-ing day.

202 Let us go in peace

Martin Foster

Let us go in peace on our pil-grim road: Christ be-fore, be-hind, Christ a-bove, be-low. 'Til we meet a-gain at our jour-ney's end when Christ will wel-come us home.

Ah

© 2003 Martin Foster

203 Let nothing trouble you

Bernadette Farrell

Accompaniment

204 Song of Simeon

Martin Foster

Response 𝄋
Pro - tect us, while a - wake; watch us, while a-sleep; that a-

wake, we may watch with Christ; and a- sleep, rest in peace.

Last time to Coda ⊕

The *Nun Dimittis* is sung at Night Prayer, at Candlemas and to bid farewell. There is an alternative Requiem refrain: see opposite

Requiem Refrain
may be substituted
for standard refrain

Re - qui-em æ - ter - nam do - na e - is, Do - mi-ne,

et lux per - pe - tu - a lu-ce-at e - is, Do - mi-ne.

Verse 1

Lord, now let your ser - vant de - part in peace, for you kept your pro - mise. Pro -

Response D.S.

Verse 2

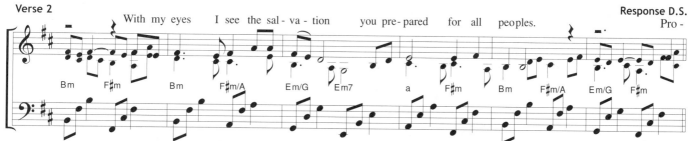

With my eyes I see the sal - va - tion you pre - pared for all peoples. Pro -

Response D.S.

wake,   we may watch__ with Christ;   and a - sleep,   rest   in peace.

Coda

205 Evening Hymn (Holden Evening Prayer)

Marty Haugen

Leader: Jesus Christ, you are the light of the world; the light no darkness can o-ver-come; Stay with us now, for it is evening,

All and the day is al-most over. Let your light scat-ter the darkness, and shine within your peo-ple here.—

1. Joy-ous light of heav'nly glo - ry, lo-ving glow of God's own
2. In the stars that grace the dark - ness, in the bla - zing sun of

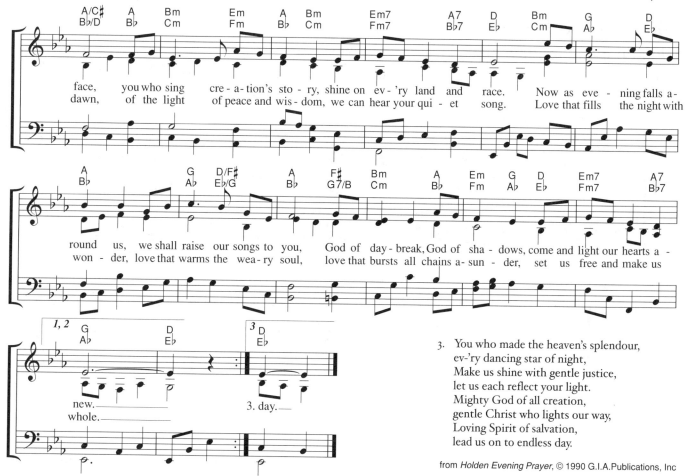

3. You who made the heaven's splendour,
   ev'ry dancing star of night,
   Make us shine with gentle justice,
   let us each reflect your light.
   Mighty God of all creation,
   gentle Christ who lights our way,
   Loving Spirit of salvation,
   lead us on to endless day.

279

206 Litany & Prayers
(Holden Evening Prayer)

Marty Haugen

Hmmm... God of mer- cy, hold us in love.

Invocations

Leader:
1. In peace,— in peace— we pray— to you:
2. For peace and sal - va - tion, we pray— to you.
3. For peace be - tween na - tions, for peace be - tween peo - ples:
4. For we who are ga - thered to wor - ship and praise you:
5. For all of your ser - vants who live out your gos - pel:
6. For all those who go - vern, that jus - tice might guide them:
7. For all those who la - bour in ser - vice to o - thers:
8. Grant wea - ther that nou - rish - es all of cre - a - tion:
9. Keep watch on our loved ones and keep us from dan - ger:
10. For all the be - lov - ved who rest in your mer - cy:

Conclusion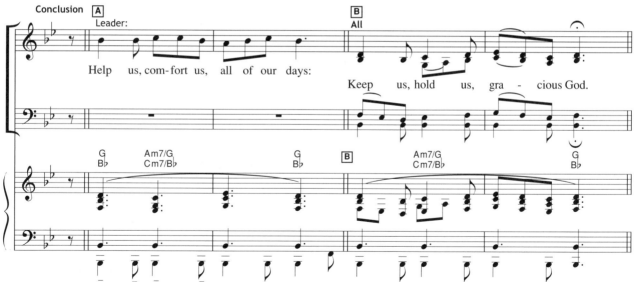

Leader: Help us, com-fort us, all of our days:

All Keep us, hold us, gra - cious God.

207 Before the ending of the day

Anonymous/Andrew Maries

Gently, like a lullaby

1. Be-fore the en-ding of the day, Cre-a-tor of the world, we pray that
2. From e-vil dreams de-fend our sight, from fears and dark-ness of the night: tread
3. Fa-ther, may what we ask be done thro' Je-sus Christ, your on-ly Son, and

(Fine)

you with stead-fast love would keep your watch a-round us when we sleep.
un-der foot our dead-ly foe that we no sin - ful thought may know.
Ho - ly Spi-rit, by whose breath our souls are raised to life from death.

(Fine)

The traditional Compline hymn. Other LM tunes may be used.

Music: *Alicia*, LM. © Andrew Maries. Words *Te lucis ante terminum*, 5th-6th Cent., tr. © Church of the Province of Melanesia

282

1. Before the ending of the day,
   Creator of the world, we pray
   that you with steadfast love would keep
   your watch around us when we sleep.

2. From evil dreams defend our sight,
   from fears and darkness of the night:
   treat under foot our deadly foe
   that we may no sinful thought may know.

3. O Father, that we ask be done
   through Jesus Christ, your only Son,
   and Holy Spirit, by whose breath
   our souls are raised to life from death.

208   Night has fallen

Malawi

gently but not sentimentally

1. *Night has fal - len.* Night has fal - len. God our ma-ker, guard us slee-ping.___ 2. *Dark-ness*

2. Darkness now has come....
3. See your children, Lord....
4. We are with you, Lord...

5. Keep us in your love...
6. Soon we go to rest...
7. Night has fallen...

Words: attr. Clement Scott, tr. by Tom Colvin Music: *Dzuwa Lapita*, Malawian; adapted Tom Colvin, arr. John L Bell
ranslation & arrangement © 1969, 1997 Hope Publishing Co. Administered by CopyCare,

Celebrating the hours of the day

The form of all celebrations of the Liturgy of the Hours
is: Introduction,
Psalmody,
Short scripture reading,
[Canticle,
Intercessions, concluding with Lord's Prayer]
Conclusion (usually a simple blessing).

This book could be used for celebrations of the principal
offices, with the leader and readers supplying the
other texts from the appropriate Office books.

Music suitable for the Office is found throughout this
book, in particular for **Evening Prayer**:
Introduction: 200
Hymn: 111, 112, 200
Lucernarium: see section *God of Light and Darkness*
Psalms: see index on p.286. Psalms associated with
evening are the Incense Psalm (141), and its
companion Psalm 142.
Psalms are the heart of the office, and they may be
prayed in many ways. For instance, the responses
may be sung with a reader reciting the verses. The
response need not even be taken from the psalm;

look at the character of each psalm (thanksgiving,
praise, lament) and find a response from the book
that is appropriate.
Magnificat: 175-177
Intercessions: see 72-84; other suggestions are: 11, 20-1,
23, 25, 44, 150-1, 155, 186

Morning Prayer:
The customary introduction is *Lord ,open our lips/And we
shal praise your name.*
Hymn: Psalm 100 (12) would be suitable
Psalms: See remarks under Evening Prayer. Suitable
psalms for morning are 51, 63, 95, 100 (traditional
morning psalms), and 107 (pure praise.)
Canticle: there is no setting of the Benedictus, but a
chant such as nos 91, 123, 181 or 189 could be sung as
a refrain with a reader reading the verses .

Midday Prayer: the hymn 132 and the psalm responses
39, 96 and 106 were written especially for this simple
office.

Night Prayer: Hymn 202 and the Canticle of Simeon
are texts for Night Prayer.

A Time of Prayer
as proposed by the Taizé community

A group of people can use the following order to pray:

> One or two opening songs
> A psalm
> Song of light (optional)
> One or two Bible readings, each followed by a song
> Silence
> Prayer of intercession or adoration
> Our Father
> Concluding prayer
> Meditative songs
> Optional conclusions:
>> Prayer around the Cross
>> or Celebration of the resurrection

Prayer around the Cross is 'a way of expressing communion not only with the crucified Jesus but with all who suffer - all victims of abuse, discrimination or torture'.

The icon of the Cross is laid down in the centre of the church, resting on low cushions or solls and illuminated by a few candles. Those who wish may come up to the Cross to pray. They may make a gesture such as placing their forehead on the wood of the Cross, as a sign that they are entrusting to Christ all their burdens and those of others, whether known to them personally or not. Meditative singing continues throughout this time.

Celebration of the Resurrection is 'the promise of our own resurrection, which already begins invisibly here on earth.' On entering the dimly-lit church, everyone is given a small candle. While a song of resurrection is sung, each person's candle is lit. Children may help with the lighting. A Gospel of the Resurrection is read, followed by more singing.

Index of Psalms

An asterisk indicates a cantor's verse within a non-psalm setting

---

Index of first lines and common titles